rockschool®

Guitar Grade 7

Performance pieces, technical exercises and in-depth guidance for Rockschool examinations

www.rockschool.co.uk

Acknowledgements

Published by Rockschool Ltd. © 2012
Catalogue Number RSK051208
ISBN: 978-1-908920-07-2

AUDIO
Recorded at Fisher Lane Studios
Produced and engineered by Nick Davis
Assistant engineer and Pro Tools operator Mark Binge
Mixed and mastered at Langlei Studios
Mixing and additional editing by Duncan Jordan
Supporting Tests recorded by Duncan Jordan and Kit Morgan
Mastered by Duncan Jordan
Executive producers: James Uings, Jeremy Ward and Noam Lederman

MUSICIANS
James Arben, Joe Bennett, Jason Bowld, Larry Carlton, Stuart Clayton, Andy Crompton, Neel Dhorajiwala, Fergus Gerrand, Charlie Griffiths, Felipe Karam, Kishon Khan, Noam Lederman, DJ Harry Love, Dave Marks, Kit Morgan, Jon Musgrave, Jake Painter, Richard Pardy, Ross Stanley, Stuart Ryan, Carl Sterling, Henry Thomas, Camilo Tirado, Simon Troup, James Uings, Steve Walker, Chris Webster, Norton York, Nir Z

PUBLISHING
Fact Files written by Joe Bennett, Charlie Griffiths, Stephen Lawson, Simon Pitt, Stuart Ryan and James Uings
Walkthroughs written by James Uings
Music engraving and book layout by Simon Troup and Jennie Troup of Digital Music Art
Proof reading and copy editing by Chris Bird, Claire Davies, Stephen Lawson, Simon Pitt and James Uings
Publishing administration by Caroline Uings
Cover design by Philip Millard

SYLLABUS
Syllabus director: Jeremy Ward
Instrumental specialists: Stuart Clayton, Noam Lederman and James Uings
Special thanks to: Brad Fuller and Georg Voros

SPONSORSHIP
Noam Lederman plays Mapex Drums, PAISTE cymbals and uses Vic Firth Sticks
Rockschool would like to thank the following companies for donating instruments used in the cover artwork

PRINTING
Printed and bound in the United Kingdom by Caligraving Ltd
CDs manufactured in the European Union by Software Logistics

DISTRIBUTION
Exclusive Distributors: Music Sales Ltd

CONTACTING ROCKSCHOOL
www.rockschool.co.uk
Telephone: +44 (0)845 460 4747
Fax: +44 (0)845 460 1960

Table of Contents

Introductions & Information

Rockschool Grade Pieces

Technical Exercises

Supporting Tests

Additional Information

Welcome to Rockschool Guitar Grade 7

Welcome to Guitar Grade 7

Welcome to the Rockschool Guitar Grade 7 pack. This book and CD contain everything you need to play guitar at this grade. In the book you will find the exam scores in both standard guitar notation and TAB. The CD has full stereo mixes of each tune, backing tracks to play along to for practice, and spoken two bar count-ins to both the full mixes and backing track versions of the songs.

Guitar Exams

At each grade, you have the option of taking one of two different types of examination:

- **Grade Exam:** a Grade Exam is a mixture of music performances, technical work and tests. You prepare three pieces (two of which may be Free Choice Pieces) and the contents of the Technical Exercise section. This accounts for 75% of the exam marks. The other 25% consists of: a Quick Study Piece (10%), a pair of instrument specific Ear Tests (10%), and finally you will be asked five General Musicianship Questions (5%). The pass mark is 60%.

- **Performance Certificate:** in a Performance Certificate you play five pieces. Up to three of these can be Free Choice Pieces. Each song is marked out of 20 and the pass mark is 60%.

Book Contents

The book is divided into a number of sections. These are:

- **Exam Pieces:** in this book you will find six specially commissioned pieces of Grade 7 standard. Each of these is preceded by a ***Fact File***. Fact Files contain a summary of the song, its style, tempo, key and technical features, along with a list of the musicians who played on it. There is additional information on the techniques and style as well as recommended listening. The song is printed on up to four pages. Immediately after each song is a ***Walkthrough***. This covers the song from a performance perspective, focusing on the technical issues you will encounter along the way. Each Walkthrough features two graphical musical 'highlights' showing particular parts of the song. Each song comes with a full mix version and a backing track. Both versions have spoken count-ins at the beginning. Please note that any solos played on the full mix versions are indicative only.

- **Technical Exercises:** you should prepare the exercises set in this grade in the keys indicated. You should also choose ***one*** Stylistic Study from the three printed to practise and play to the backing track in the exam. The style you choose will determine the style of the Quick Study Piece.

- **Supporting Tests and General Musicianship Questions:** in Guitar Grade 7 there are three supporting tests – a Quick Study Piece, a pair of Ear Tests and a set of General Musicianship Questions (GMQs) asked at the end of each exam. Examples of the types of tests likely to appear in the exam are printed in this book. Additional test examples of both types of test and the GMQs can be found in the Rockschool *Guitar Companion Guide*.

- **Grade 8 Preview:** we have included in this book one of the songs found in the Grade 8 Guitar book as a taster. The piece is printed with its Fact File and Walkthrough and the full mix can be found on the CD.

- **General Information:** finally, you will find information on exam procedures, including online examination entry, marking schemes, and what to do when arriving, and waiting, for your exam.

We hope you enjoy using this book. You will find a *Syllabus Guide* for Guitar and other exam information on our website: *www.rockschool.co.uk*. Rockschool Graded Music Exams are accredited in England, Wales and Northern Ireland by Ofqual, the DfE and CCEA and by SQA Accreditation in Scotland.

SONG TITLE: THE PANTS ERA
GENRE: METAL
TEMPO: 100 BPM
KEY: E MINOR

TECH FEATURES: ALTERNATE PICKING
ODD TIME SIGNATURES
AND HARMONICS

COMPOSER: CHARLIE GRIFFITHS

PERSONNEL: CHARLIE GRIFFITHS (GTR)
DAVE MARKS (BASS)
JASON BOWLD (DRUMS)

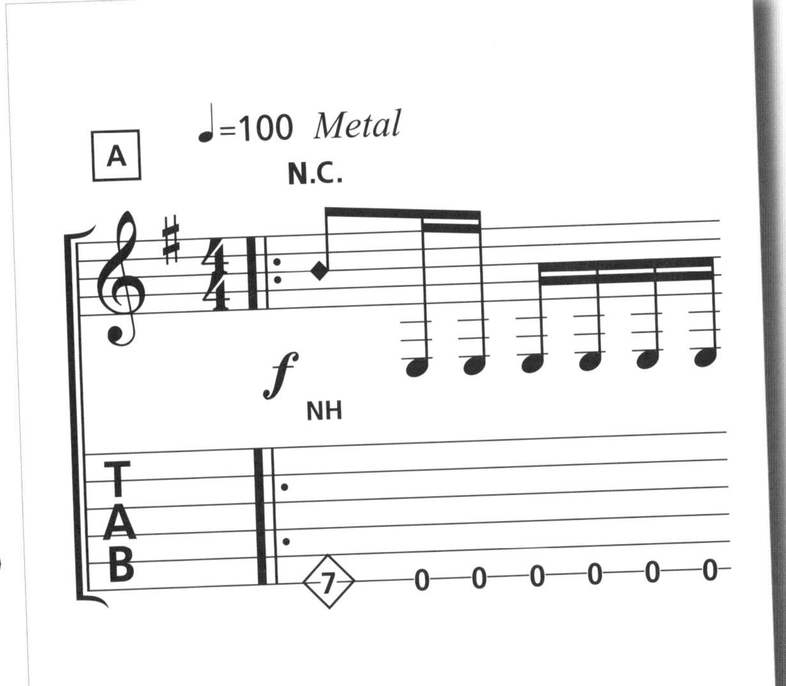

OVERVIEW

'The Pants Era' is a slab of groove metal in the style of bands like Pantera, Lamb of God, Korn and Fear Factory. It starts with a natural harmonic riff that transforms into a pounding verse riff followed by a pre-chorus in 7/8 time. The chorus is the most challenging part of the song and requires positional shifts and intense alternate picking.

STYLE FOCUS

Groove metal is a branch of the thrash metal movement that relies on powerful, heavily distorted riffs and syncopated rhythms that are often solidly locked into the drum part with particular focus on the kick drums. The blues scale and powerchords are favoured with groove metal; a strong focus is placed on technical ornamentation such as palm muting, harmonics and plenty of vibrato.

THE BIGGER PICTURE

This style of metal was brought into the mainstream in 1990 by American metal band Pantera. Their groundbreaking album *Cowboys From Hell* (1990) helped them to dominate the scene for the entire decade. Guitarist Dimebag Darrell and his drummer brother Vinnie Paul created a style of aggressive yet precise riffing with an unparalleled rhythmic power that became the blueprint for the genre that is still used to this day. Since Pantera disbanded in 2003 and Dimebag's untimely death in 2004, bands like Lamb of God and Killswitch Engage have filled the void, spearheading a resurgence of interest in the genre. More recently, bands such as Meshuggah and Periphery have taken the style to new, more rhythmically complex heights.

RECOMMENDED LISTENING

The title track from Pantera's *Cowboys From Hell* is the nucleus of groove metal. Next came the metal classic 'Walk' from their more aggressive follow-up album *Vulgar Display Of Power* (1992). Lamb of God's 'Redneck' from *Sacrament* (2006) could be viewed as a tribute to Dimebag's signature riffing style, such is the similarity. Killswitch Engage demonstrated deft guitar and drum unison work on 'My Last Serenade' from their acclaimed album *Alive Or Just Breathing* (2002). Meshuggah's 'Stengah' from *Nothing* (2002) illustrates that rhythmic complexity is no barrier to groove, while Periphery's 'Icarus Lives!' from their 2010 eponymous debut is one of the catchiest riffs to emerge in recent years.

The Pants Era

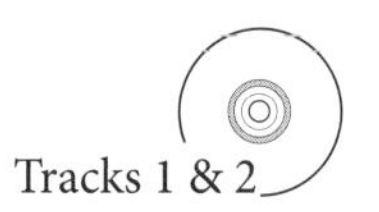

Charlie Griffiths

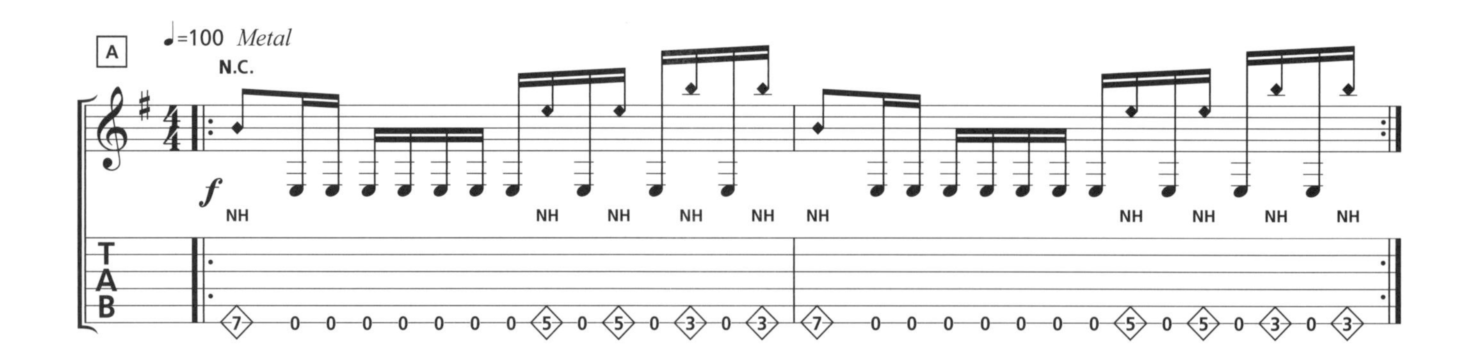

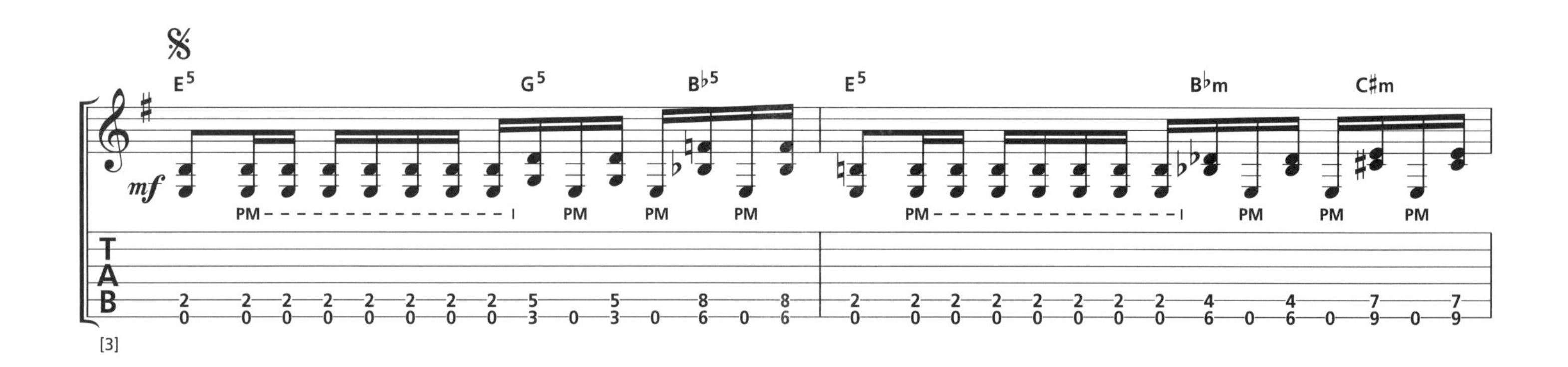

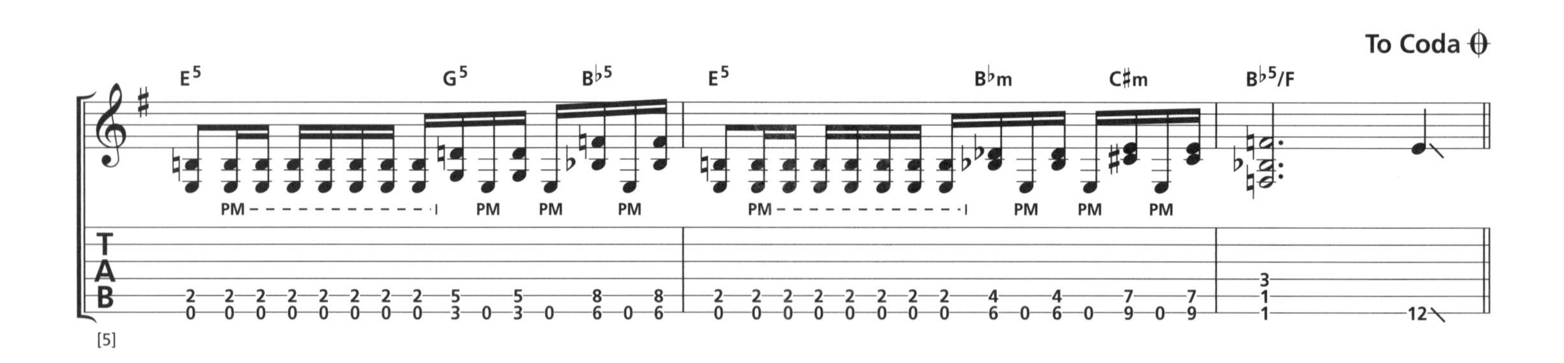

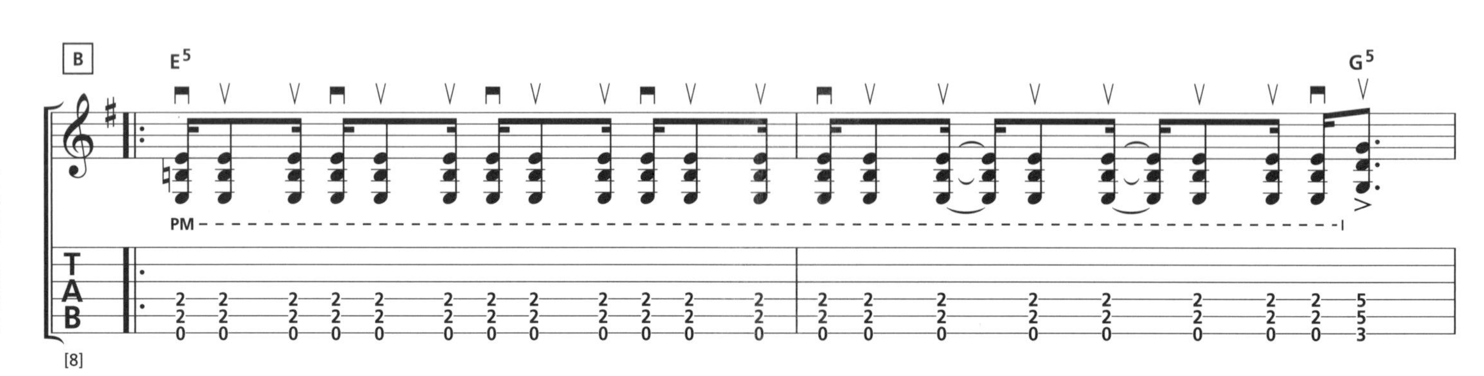

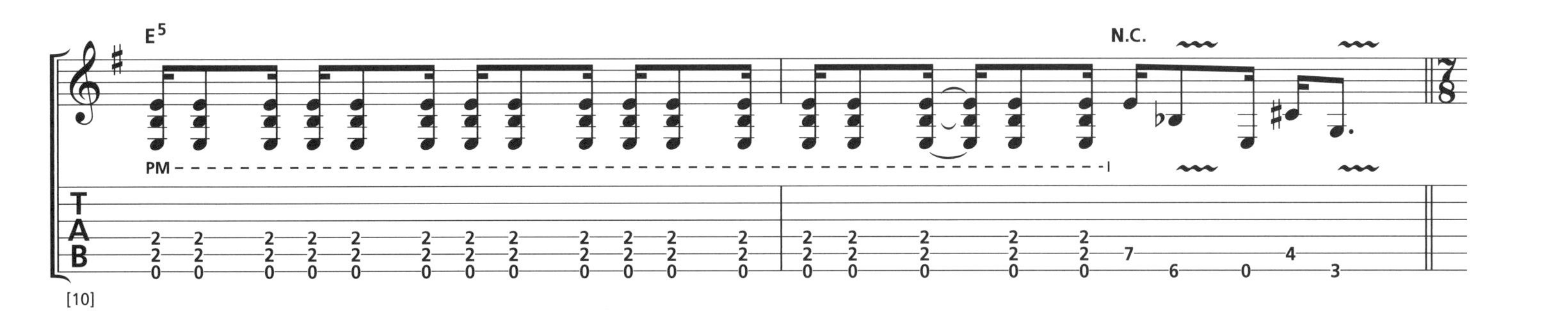
E5
N.C.
PM
T
A
B
[10]

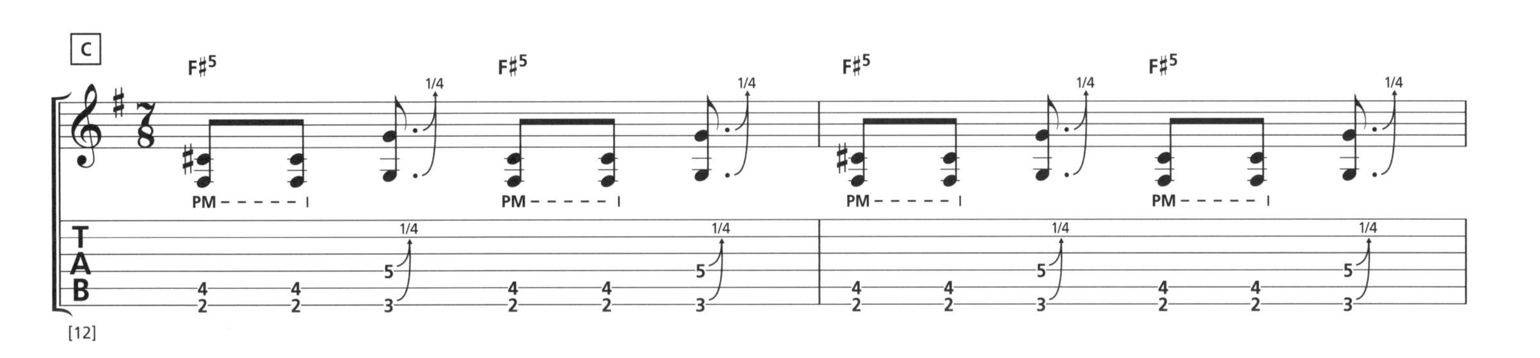
C
F♯5
1/4
PM
T
A
B
[12]

F♯5
N.C.
1/4
PM
T
A
B
[14]

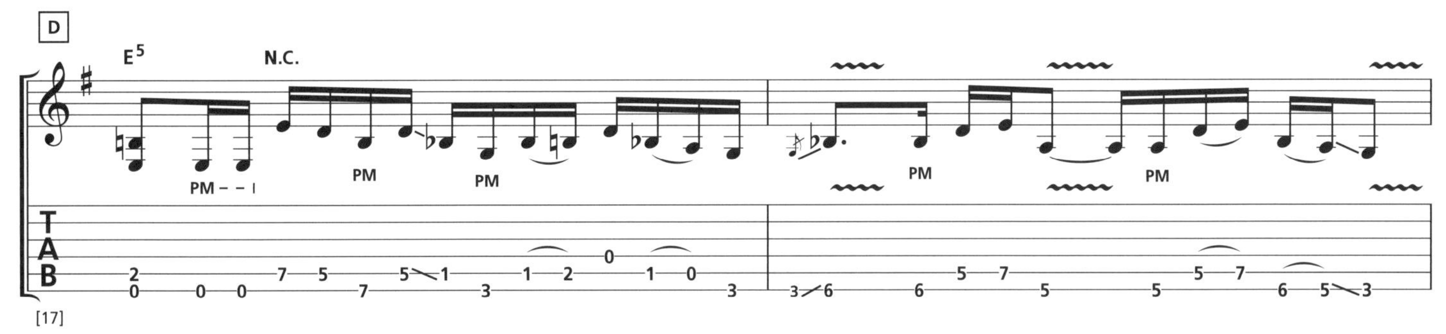
D
E5
N.C.
PM
T
A
B
[17]

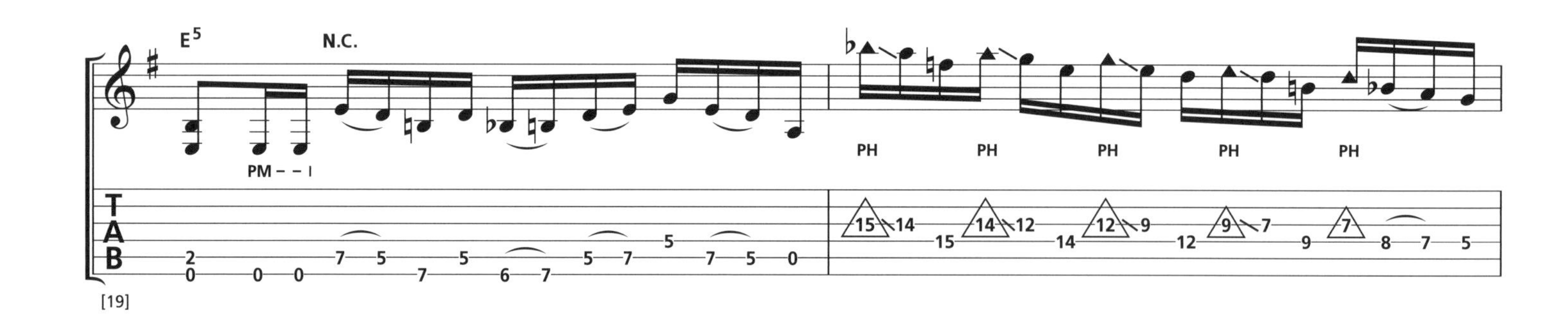
E5
N.C.
PM
PH
[19]

E5
N.C.
PM
[21]

1.
2.
E5
N.C.
PM
Rit.
BU
[23]

[26]

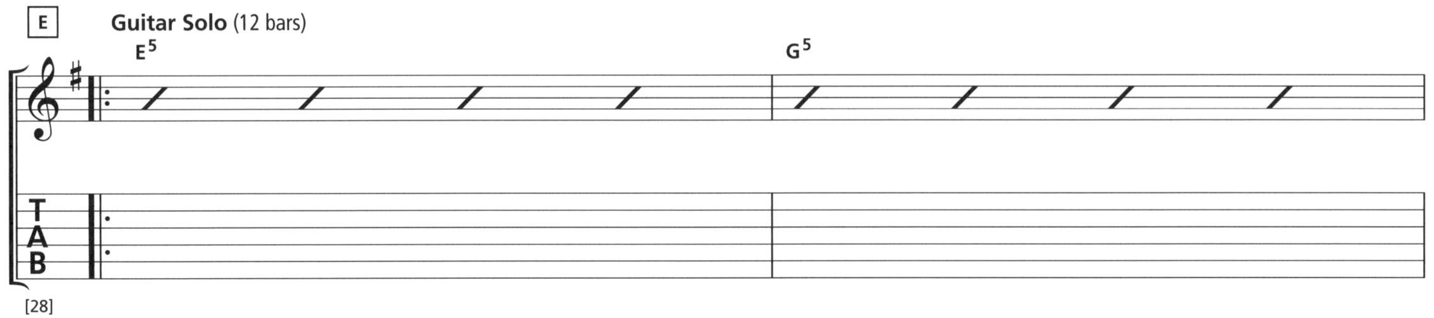
E
Guitar Solo (12 bars)
E5
G5
TAB
[28]

D.S. al Coda
Play 3 times

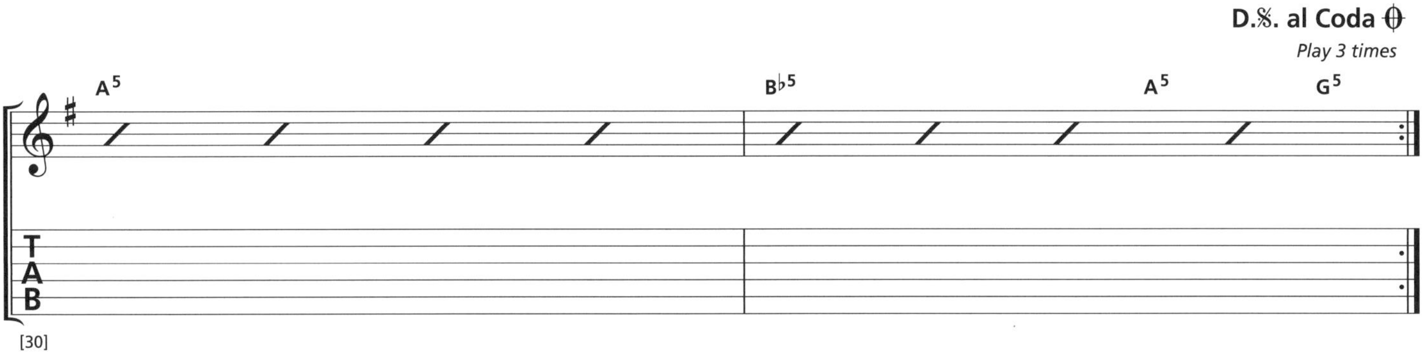
A5
B♭5
A5
G5
TAB
[30]

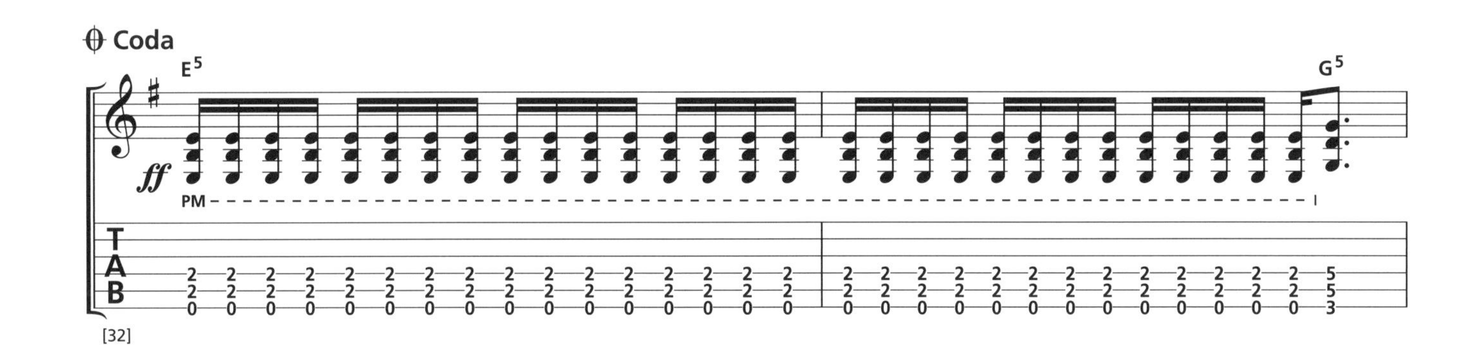
Coda
E5
G5
ff
PM
TAB
[32]

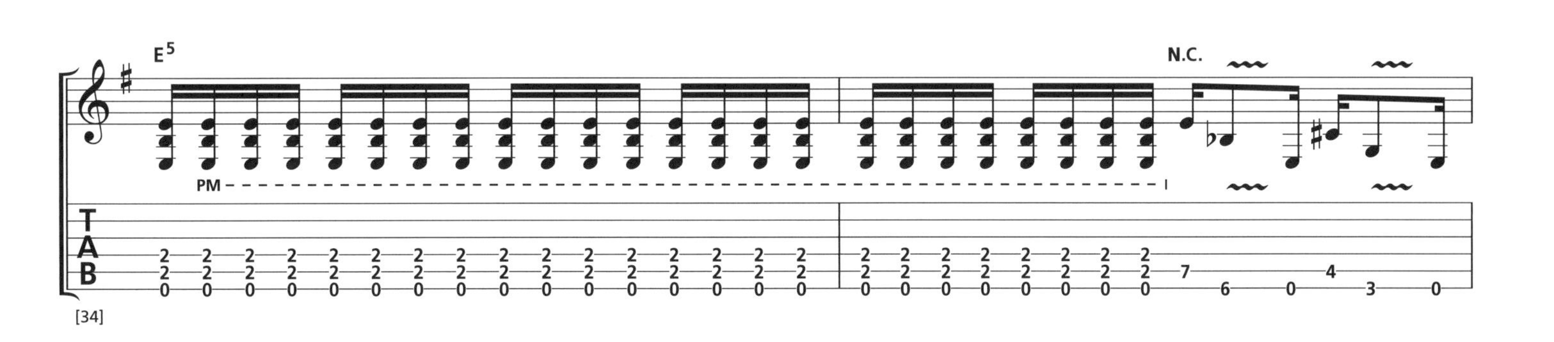
E5
N.C.
PM
TAB
[34]

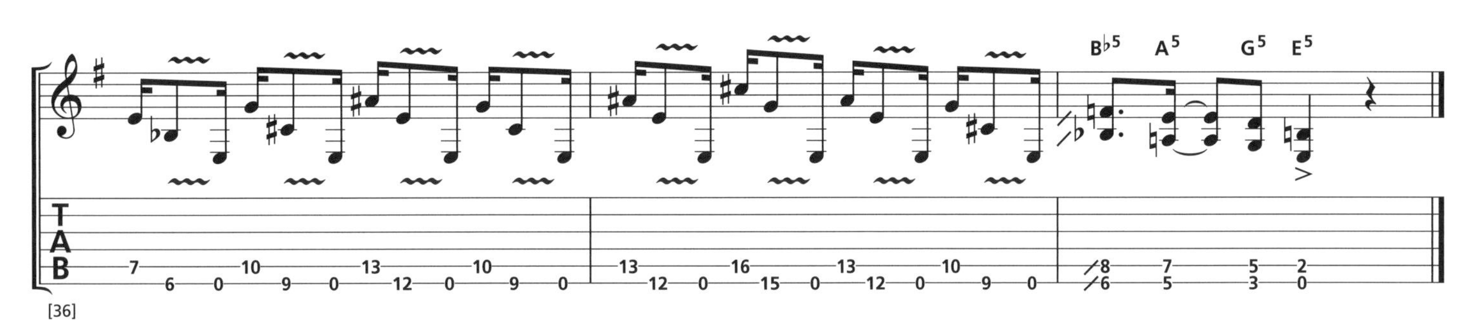
B♭5
A5
G5
E5
TAB
[36]

Walkthrough

Amp Settings

The metal rhythm guitar tone consists of two key elements: a modern high-gain distortion and a scooped tone. A scooped tone is achieved by boosting the treble and bass controls and cutting or 'scooping out' the middle. When combined with the extreme distortion this creates a heavy, aggressive tone. Add more middle to your lead tone if you wish.

Distortion Channel | Equalisation | Reverb

GAIN | BASS | MIDDLE | TREBLE | DRY – WET

A Section (Bars 1–7)

The A section starts with a riff that combines the open E string with natural harmonics. This riff is then developed using two-note chords.

Bars 1–2 | *3rd fret harmonics*

3rd fret harmonics are a little different from those found at the 5th, 7th and 12th frets. Rather than placing your finger directly over the fret, you should place your finger *slightly* in front of the fret (towards the 4th fret).

B & C Sections (Bars 8–16)

Here is a chunky syncopated, palm-muted riff that ends with a tri-tone motif developed in the coda. The C section is a seemingly complex riff that uses odd time signatures and octave bends before finishing with a scalic run.

Bars 12–16 | *Odd time signatures*

Although these signatures look complex, the riffs have a strong groove so you may find you can learn them by ear. If you struggle with any sections, try counting the rhythms in groups of the smallest time unit that can be used to successfully divide the bar. In this case, 16th notes (Fig. 1).

Bar 15 | *11/16 time signature*

When playing the 11/16 bar, it helps to ignore the time signature and simply continue playing the riff that was established in the previous three bars. When the second A♯ is played, mentally count this as beat one (it's the first note of the bar of 4/4), listen for the hi-hat on beat two then play the descending riff starting on beat three.

Bars 12–16 | *Octave bends*

These octave bends are performed by pulling both strings down towards the floor. This not a precise movement and it is almost impossible to bend the strings by the same amount. In fact, it is the discordance created by the 'inaccurate' bends that gives the riff its unique sound.

D Section (Bars 17–27)

The D section is a single-note riff that uses different techniques. There are many complex phrases in this section and you will have to break them down into individual beats to work on fingerings, pick directions and overall accuracy.

Bar 20 | *Pinch harmonic slides*

In this phrase you will play the pinch harmonic on the first of each sequence of three notes then slide down the fretboard to the next note. The harmonic sound will carry on to the next note.

E Section (Bars 28–38)

The E section is the guitar solo. The song finishes by reprising part of the A section before developing part of the B section.

Bars 28–31 | *Guitar solo*

The minor pentatonic and blues scales are popular in groove metal. You can also use the natural minor scale with the ♭5 added (Fig. 2). This will give you more note choices, while retaining the bluesy quality that is typical of the style.

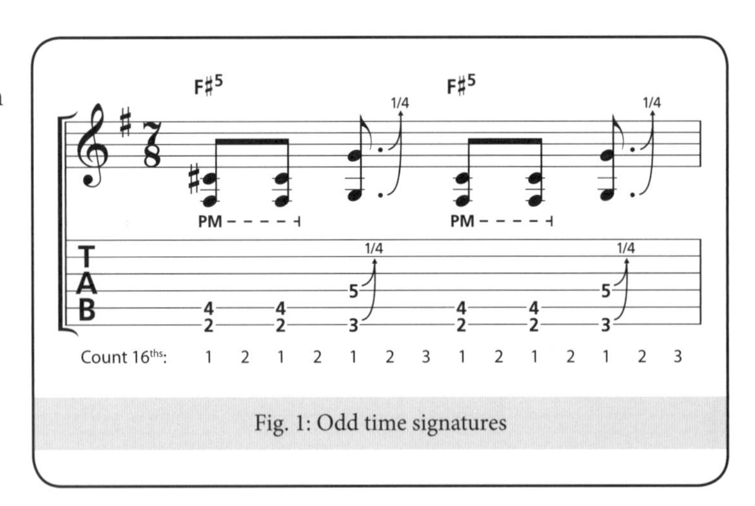

Fig. 1: Odd time signatures

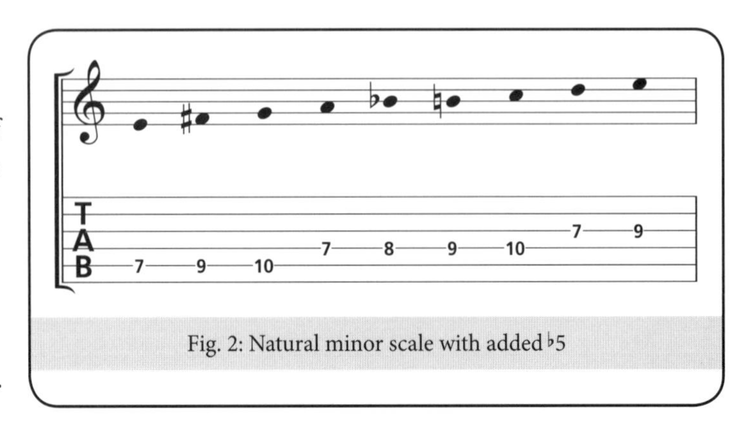

Fig. 2: Natural minor scale with added ♭5

SONG TITLE: SOMA
GENRE: BLUES
TEMPO: 55 BPM
KEY: B MINOR

TECH FEATURES: FAST LEGATO RUNS
NATURAL HARMONIC MELODIES
STRING BENDS

COMPOSER: SIMON TROUP

PERSONNEL: STUART RYAN (GTR)
HENRY THOMAS (BASS)
NOAM LEDERMAN (DRUMS)
ROSS STANLEY (KEYS)

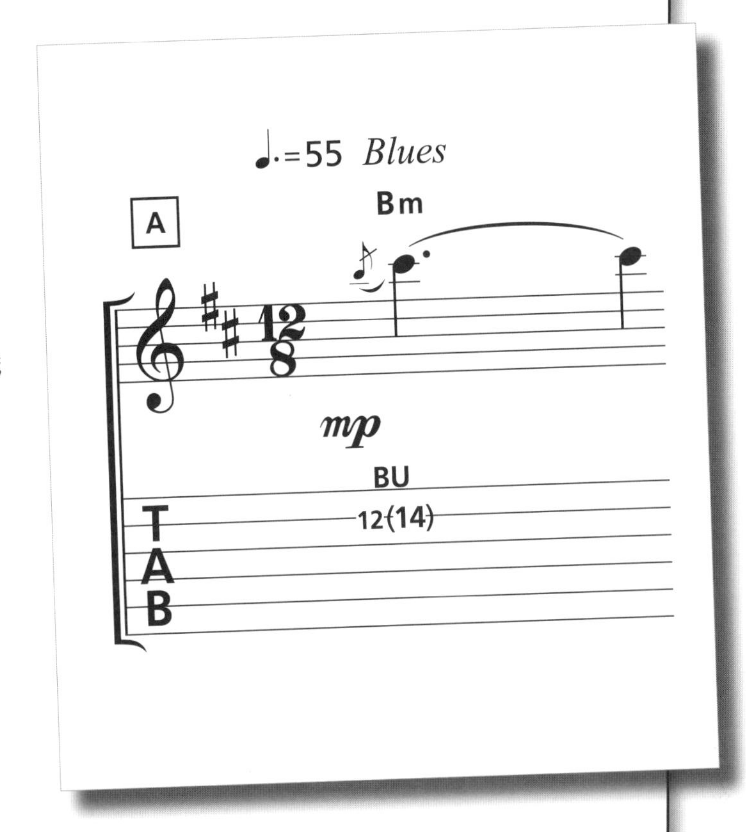

OVERVIEW

'Soma' is a homage to the distinctive guitar style of Jeff Beck. There are some typical Beck style devices laced throughout this piece from long, sustained notes with controlled vibrato to precise bends and rapid triplet licks leading into melodic phrases. In addition, there are some rapid legato passages and a melody that is played entirely in natural harmonics.

STYLE FOCUS

Beck is one of the most distinctive electric guitar players of the last 50 years. Many have tried to emulate his idiosyncratic playing style, but few can match his control and emotion when playing. The two key elements of his style are his use of picking hand fingers to pluck all the notes and his extraordinary control of the whammy bar. Another major feature is his ability to play and write melody lines with natural harmonics – and not just at the frets where these are easy to execute.

THE BIGGER PICTURE

Jeff Beck first came to prominence during the British Blues Boom of the 1960s. He was a contemporary of Eric Clapton and Led Zeppelin's Jimmy Page. All three guitarists played in The Yardbirds. Indeed, Beck replaced Clapton as guitarist in 1965 and soon attracted the attention of blues rock fans and those from further afield.

Beck is best known to casual listeners for his version of the hit single 'Hi Ho Silver Lining', which appeared in the charts in 1967, although he didn't pen the song himself and soon turned his back on this pop sound and pursued instrumental music. He chose to develop his unique style with forays into blues, jazz, rock, fusion, rockabilly and, more recently, modern electronic styles.

RECOMMENDED LISTENING

Jeff Beck's Guitar Shop (1989) is the quintessential Beck record, juxtaposing ballads with heavier rock fusion tracks. *Live At Ronnie Scotts* (2008) features him alongside some of the world's greatest session musicians, and serves as an introduction to his back catalogue in a modern setting. His most recent album, *Emotion & Commotion* (2010), is worth listening to for his soaring guitar lines. Gary Moore's 'Parisienne Walkways' is another example of this type of instrumental rock music. It reached the UK top 10 in 1979 and was co-written by Thin Lizzy's Phil Lynott.

Soma

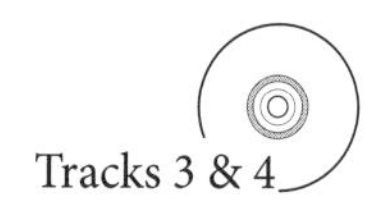

Simon Troup

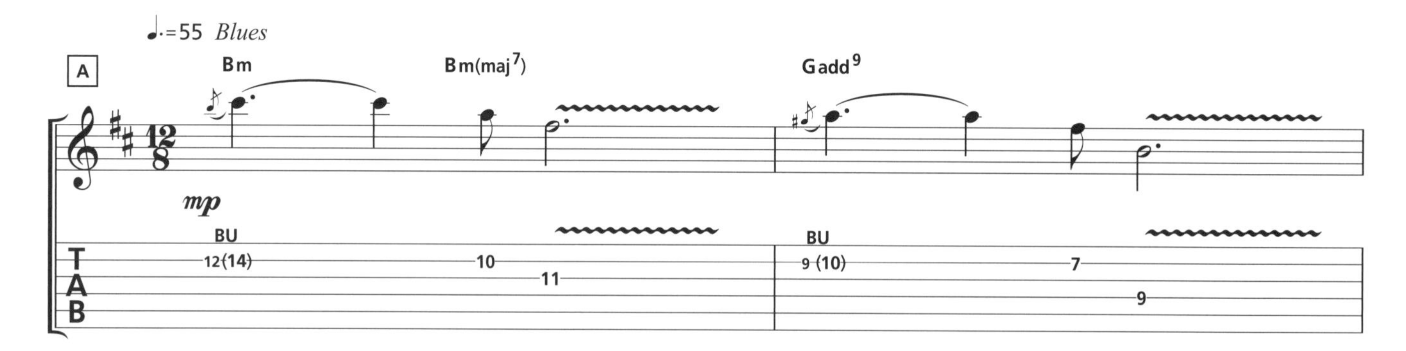

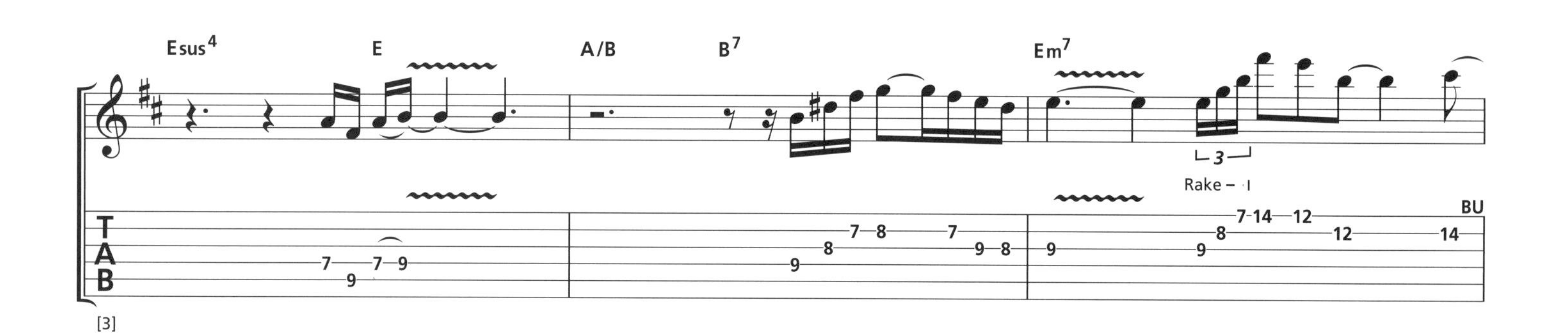

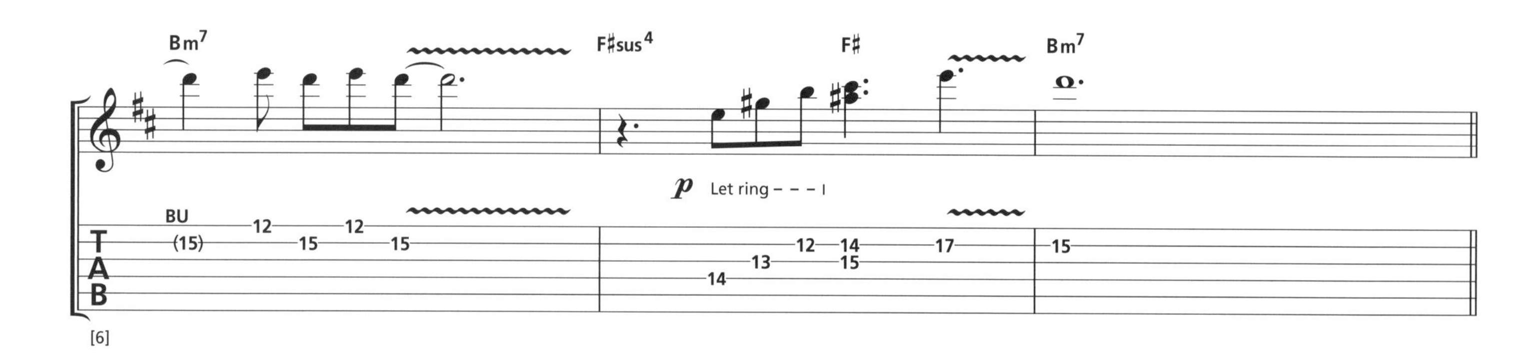

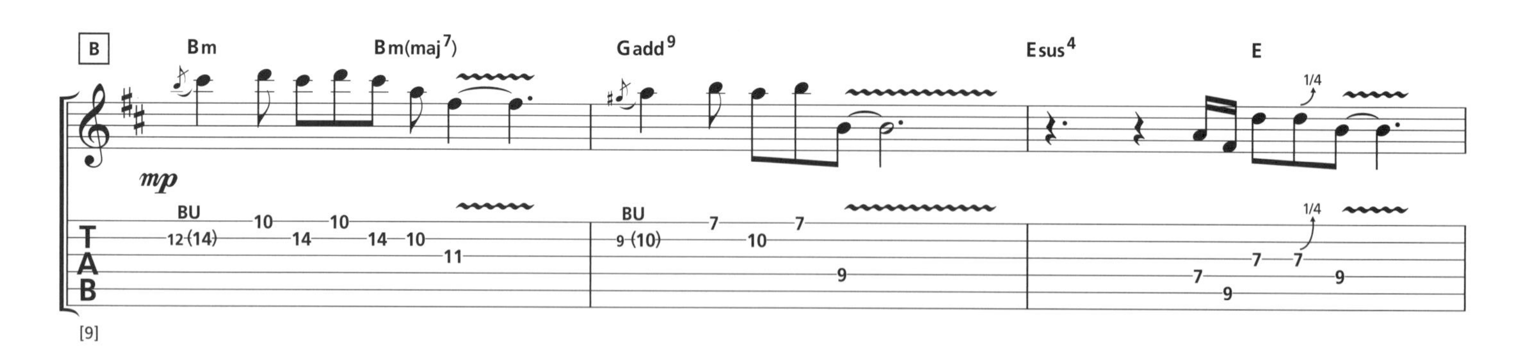

Bm7
(8va)
F♯sus4
F♯
Bm7
BU BD
NH†
T
A
B
[14]
C
Dmaj7
Gmaj7
Esus2
Em
G/A
A
8va
(NH)
[17]
† = Add vibrato where suitable by bending strings behind the nut
Dmaj7
Gmaj7
Esus2
Em
G/A
A
(8va)
(NH)
[21]
D
Guitar Solo (10 bars)
Bm
Bm(maj7)
Gadd9
Em
[25]
Bm
Em
Bm
[28]
F♯7
Bm
F♯sus4
F♯
Bm7
Ral.
p
Let ring
[31]

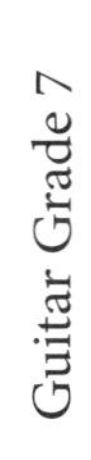
Guitar Grade 7

Walkthrough

Amp Settings

Aim for a smooth, overdriven tone that sounds aggressive and distorted when played hard but virtually clean when played softly. Adding reverb, if available, will enhance the long, sustained notes in this track but be careful not to drown the guitar.

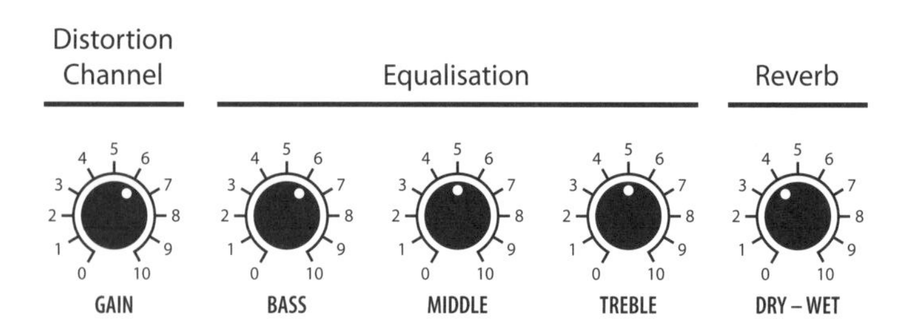

A Section (Bars 1–8)

The A section is an expressive melody that uses bends and vibrato to give a vocal quality to the part.

Bar 1 | *Re-enforced bends*
Whenever you bend a string, use all available fingers to push it up. This will give you more control and make it easier to hit the target note (the note in brackets). You can use this technique to play the bend in bar 1. Use your third finger supported by your first and second fingers.

Bars 2–6 | *Semitone bends*
Semitone bends are often overbent by lots of guitarists who are used to the whole tone bends found in pentatonic solos. Playing the target note before you attempt the bend will help with accuracy because the target note is fresh in your mind (Fig. 1). If you find you still have trouble, practise the bend slowly so that you have time to process the change of pitch.

B Section (Bars 9–16)

The B section develops the A section melody by adding more rhythmic interest and some fast, flowing scalic runs.

Bars 12–14 | *Scalic runs*
Work through the two runs in small chunks (e.g. groups of six notes). Deciding upon a fingering before you increase the speed of the phrase will give you a solid foundation to build from. Fig. 2 shows one option for the run in bar 14.

C Section (Bars 17–24)

The C section features a melody made up of natural harmonics. This melody requires fast position shifts and accurate finger placement.

Bars 17–24 | *Natural harmonics*
Natural harmonics are sounded by placing your finger lightly and *directly over* the frets. Don't make contact with any part of the fretboard because this will choke the notes. Your finger placement for the 5th and 7th fret harmonics must be fairly precise, so work through this challenging phrase slowly to begin with.

Bars 20–24 | *3rd fret harmonics*
3rd fret harmonics are different from those found at the 5th, 7th and 12th frets. Rather than placing your finger directly over the fret, you must place it *slightly* in front of the fret (i.e. towards the 4th fret).

D Section (Bars 25–34)

The D section is the guitar solo, based in B minor. The final two bars are a repeat of a phrase in the A section.

Bars 25–32 | *Guitar solo*
The B blues, minor pentatonic and natural minor scales can be used for most of the solo. The only exceptions are the Bm(maj7) in bar 26 and the F♯7 in bar 31. These chords all contain A♯ which isn't found in these scales. You will either have to adjust your phrases to play A♯ notes instead of A notes, use the relevant arpeggio over these chords or switch to the B harmonic minor scale at the appropriate time.

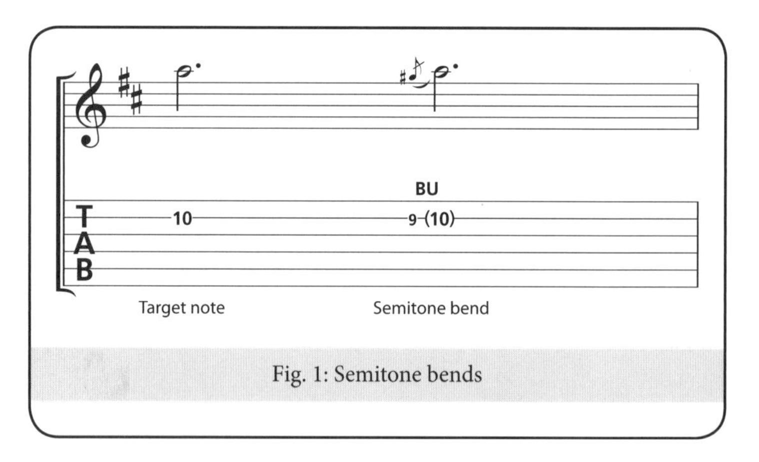

Fig. 1: Semitone bends

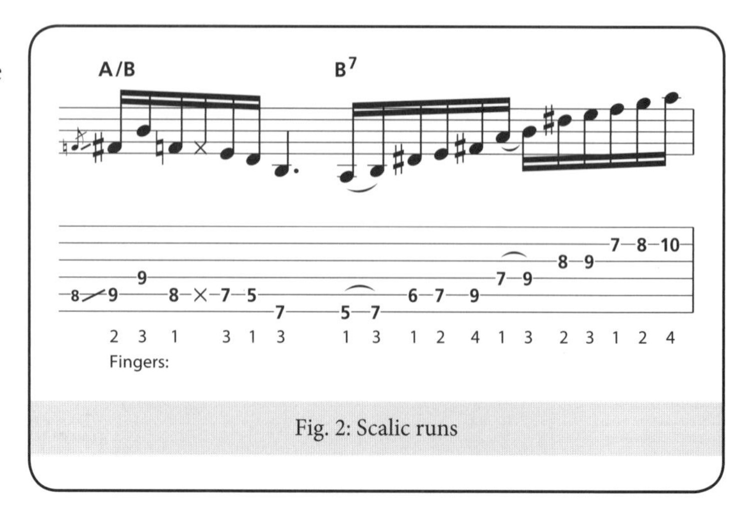

Fig. 2: Scalic runs

Broadway And 9th

SONG TITLE: BROADWAY AND 9TH
GENRE: JAZZ
TEMPO: 142 BPM
KEY: B MINOR

TECH FEATURES: OCTAVE MELODIES
CHORD MELODIES
COMPING A SOLO

COMPOSER: STUART RYAN

PERSONNEL: STUART RYAN (GTR)
HENRY THOMAS (BASS)
NOAM LEDERMAN (DRUMS)
ROSS STANLEY (KEYS)

OVERVIEW

'Broadway And 9th' is a jazz composition in the style of American jazz guitar luminary Wes Montgomery. In keeping with Montgomery's playing, 'Broadway And 9th' features octave guitar parts, chord melodies and legato phrasing. The solo sections draw from the B dorian mode, which is common to jazz improvisation. Fluency in this type of scale is an essential facet of this genre's guitar style.

STYLE FOCUS

Jazz is one of the most demanding styles of music a guitarist will play. There is a strong emphasis on improvisation, often over chords which change rapidly, making the guitarist's role as soloist a great challenge. The secret to playing over such changes is to become familiar with jazz harmony. More so than in other genres, songs are described as chord sequences plucked from the Roman numeral system (I ii iii IV V vi VII).

Once a student of jazz has gleaned an understanding of harmony theory he will devote his time to learning scales and arpeggios, which can be used as the basis of improvised solos (though always with reference to the underlying chords).

THE BIGGER PICTURE

Montgomery is not only one of the key figures of jazz *guitar* but of the genre as a whole. He came to the guitar relatively late at the age of 19 in 1942. However, he quickly developed an astonishing ability as lead player, accompanist and composer, and was soon performing regularly in his native Indiana. Unlike any guitarist before him, Montgomery chose to pick and strum with his right hand thumb. This idiosyncrasy gave him a rounded, warm tone that found favour with other guitarists and listeners alike. Another major feature of his style was his love of playing melody lines in octaves, a challenging technique he could execute at high speeds.

RECOMMENDED LISTENING

Montgomery's album *The Incredible Jazz Guitar Of Wes Montgomery (1960)* features his famous compositions 'Four On Six' and 'West Coast Blues'. This album is a great introduction to his accessible, bluesy playing. The thumb octave style and his solos throughout are inspirational. Montgomery recorded in many formats, from organ trios with Hammond player Jimmy Smith to full orchestral backings. Other essential albums are the live *Smokin' At The Half Note* (1964) and *Boss Guitar* (1962).

Broadway And 9th

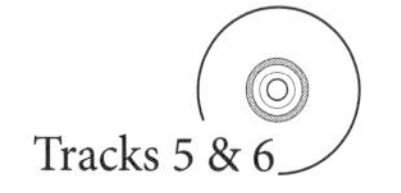

Stuart Ryan

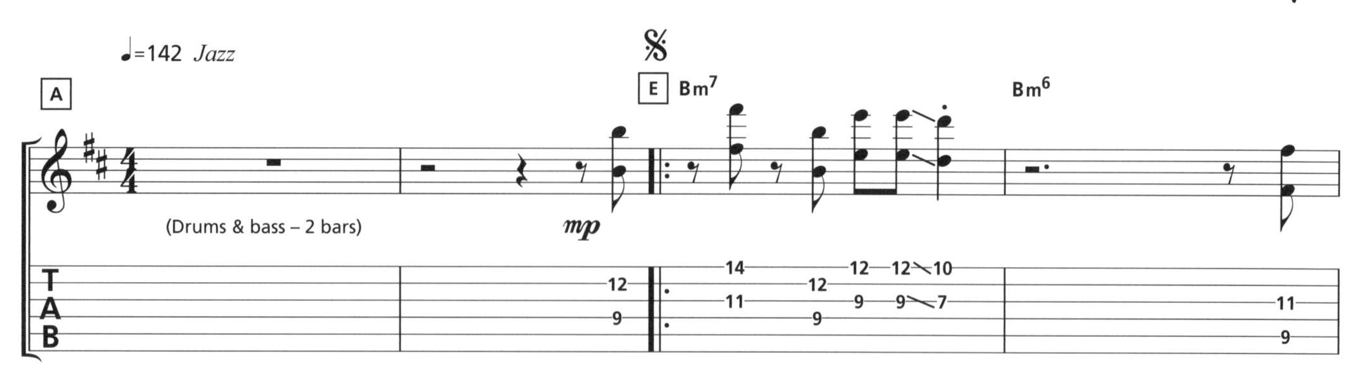

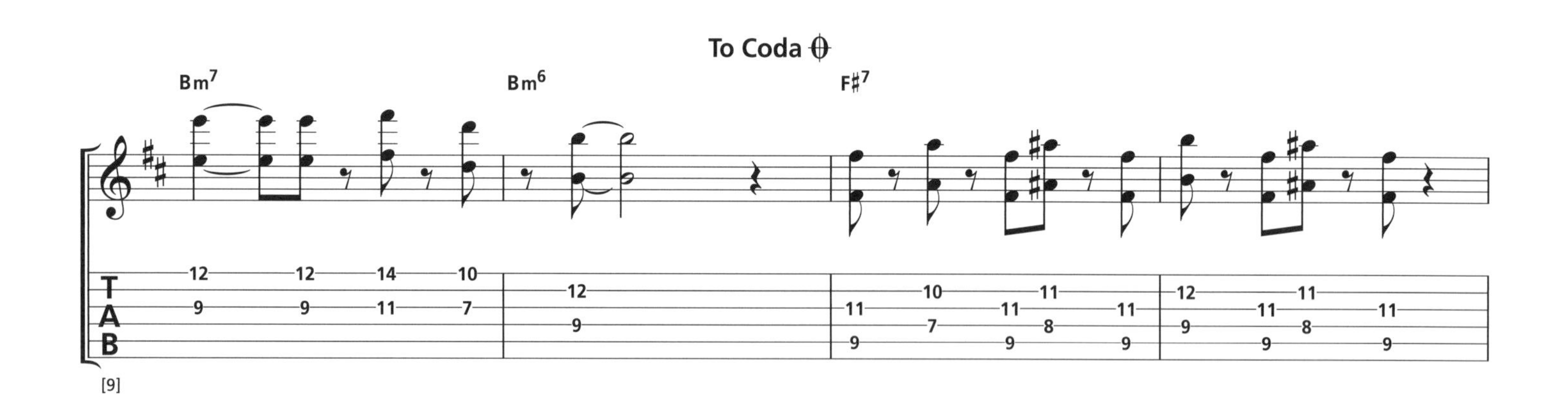

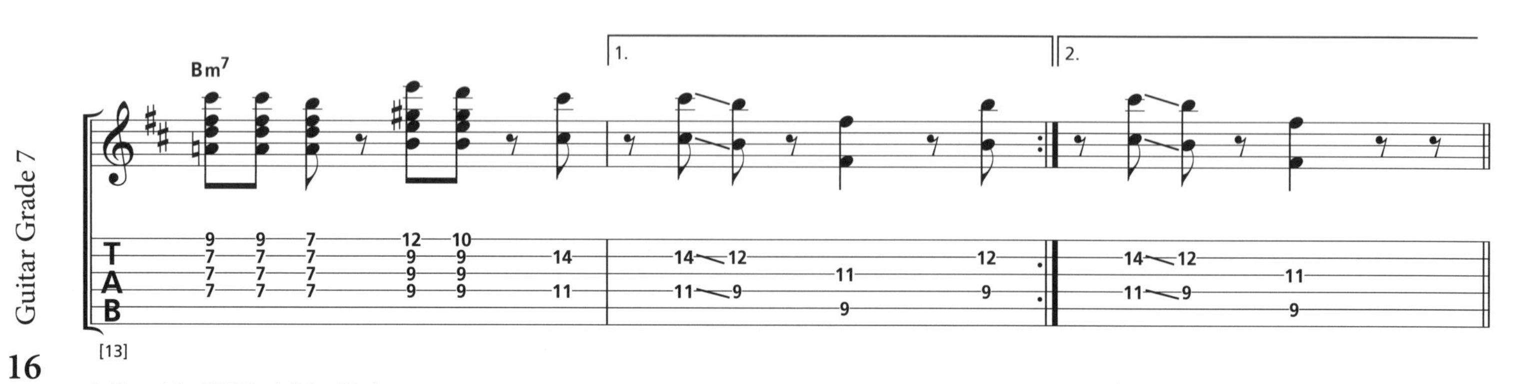

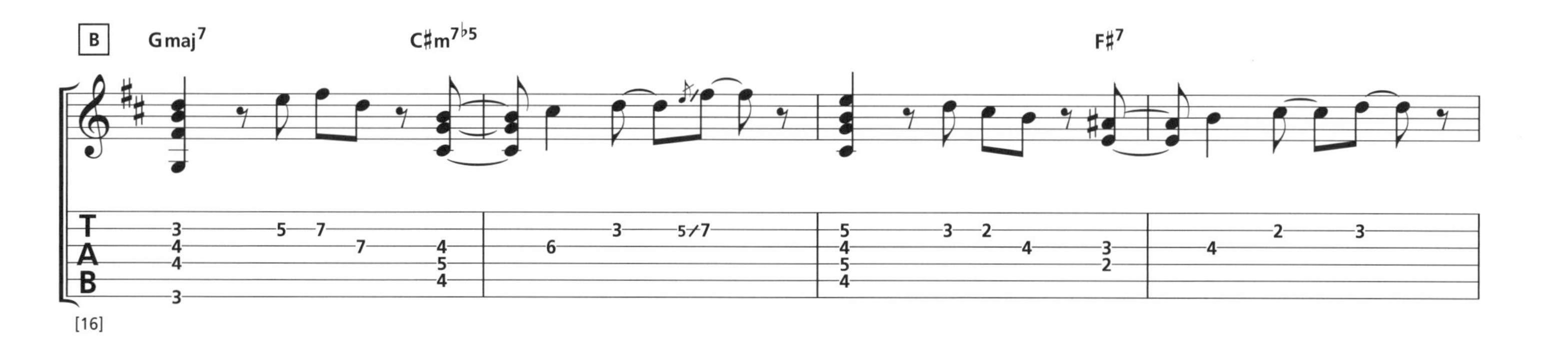
B
Gmaj7
C♯m7♭5
F♯7
[16]

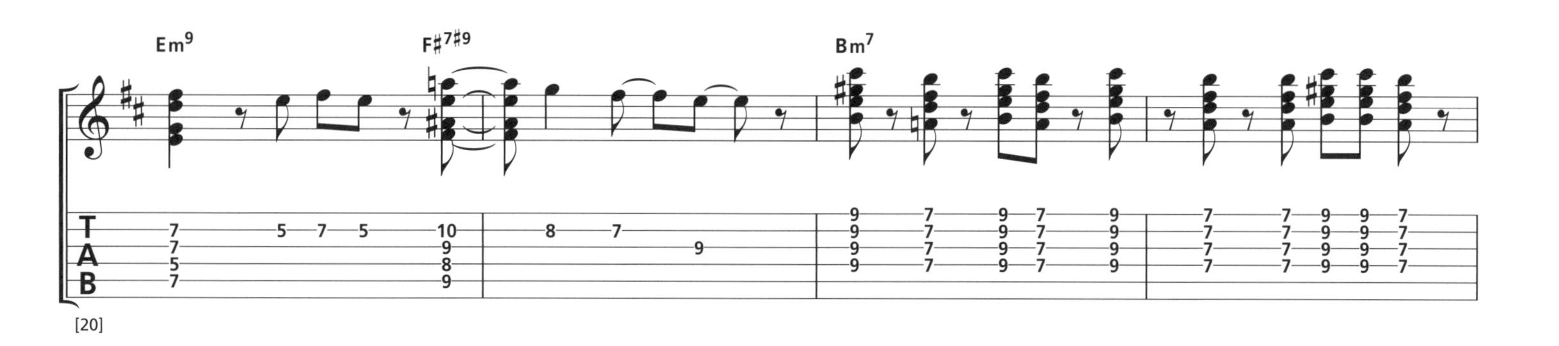
Em9
F♯7♯9
Bm7
[20]

N.C.
F♯7♯9
[24]

N.C.
[27]

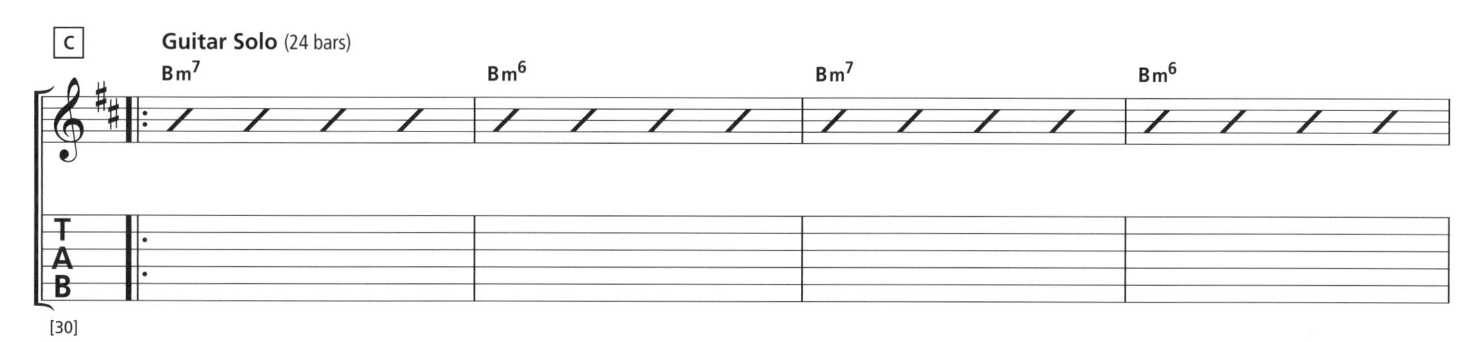
C
Guitar Solo (24 bars)
Bm7
Bm6
Bm7
Bm6
[30]

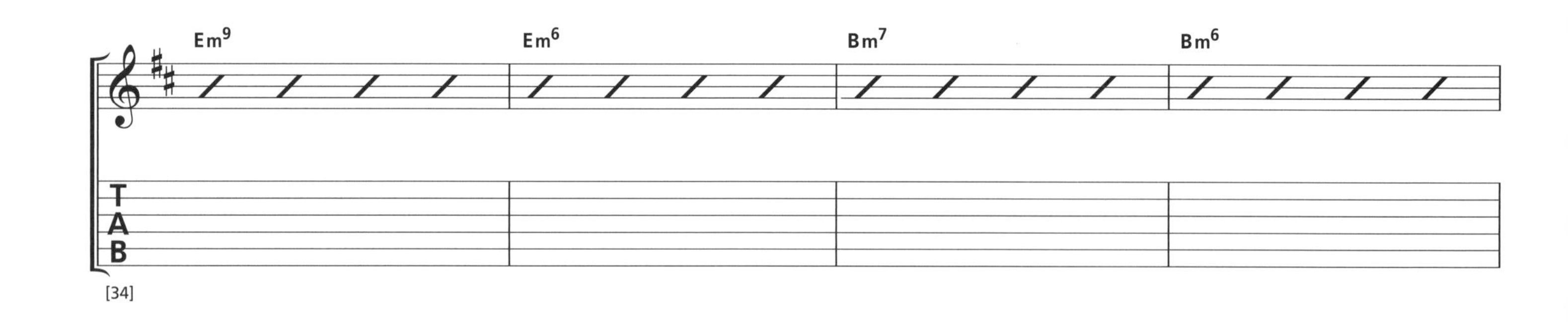
Em9
Em6
Bm7
Bm6
[34]

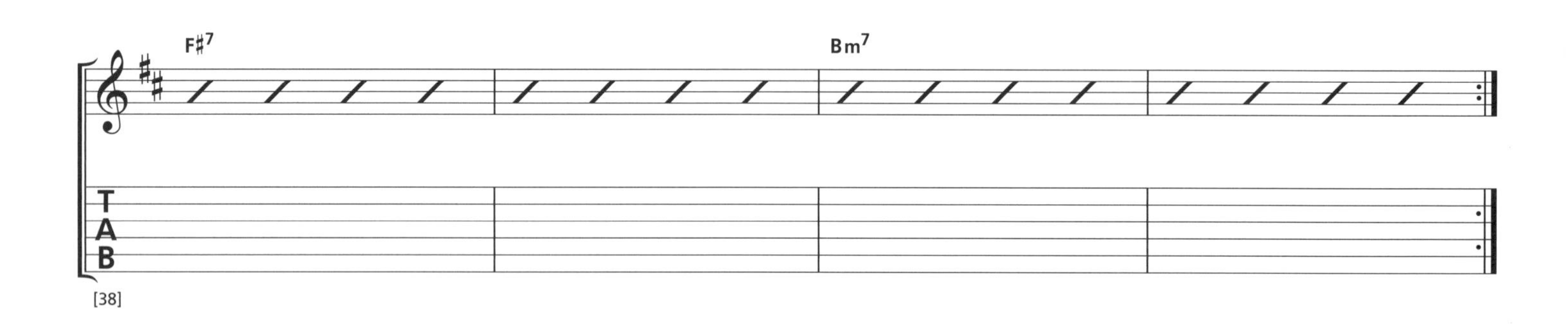
F♯7
Bm7
[38]

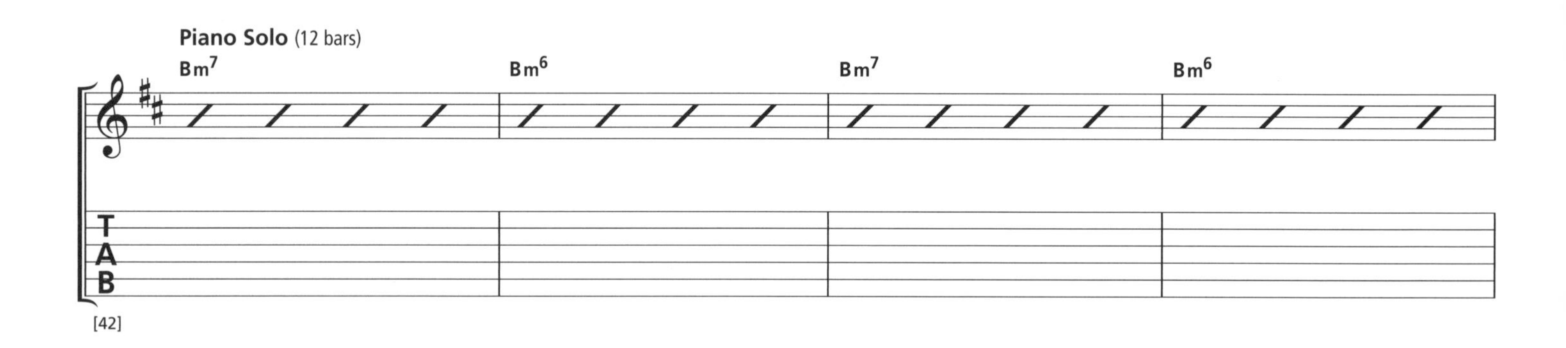
Piano Solo (12 bars)
Bm7
Bm6
Bm7
Bm6
[42]

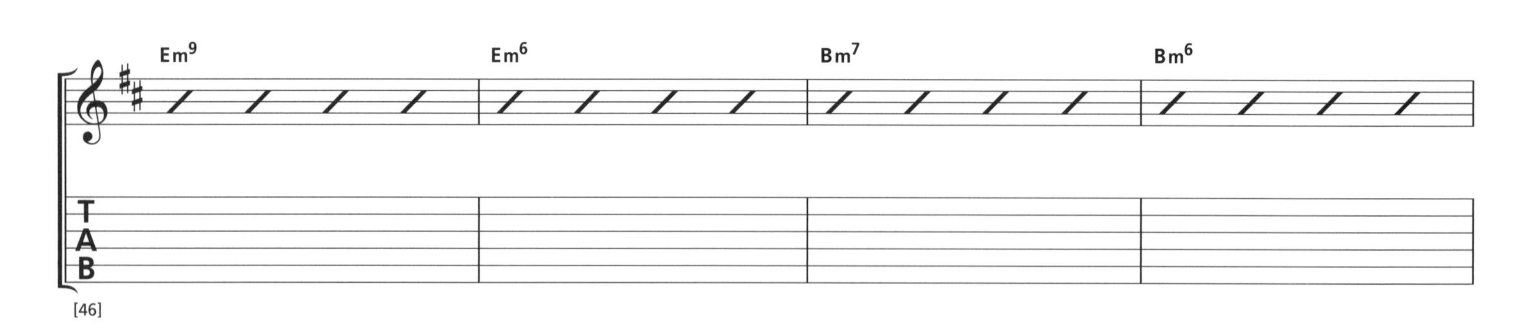
Em9
Em6
Bm7
Bm6
[46]

Guitar Grade 7

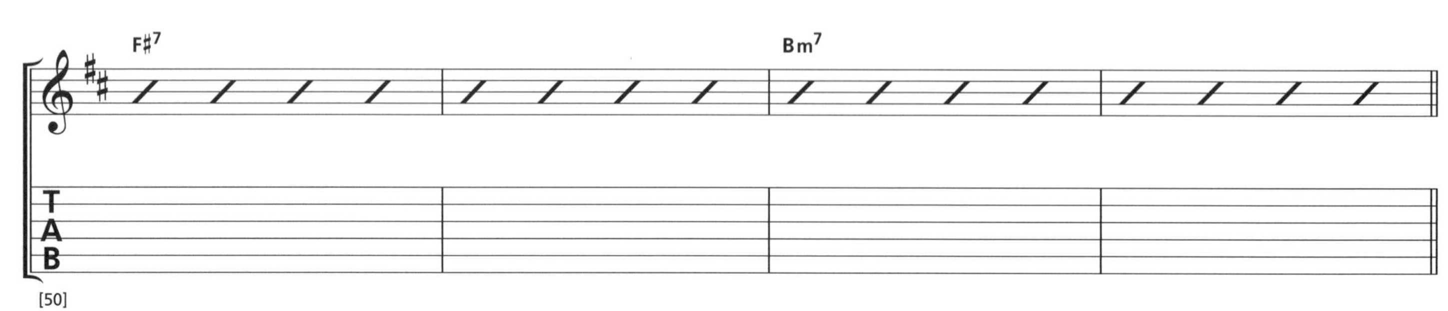
F♯7
Bm7
[50]

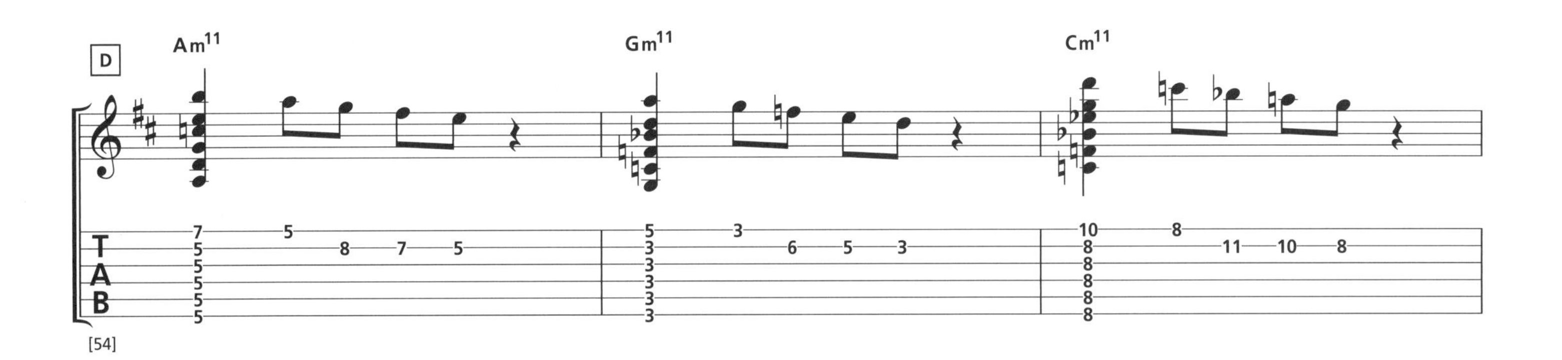
D
Am11
Gm11
Cm11
[54]

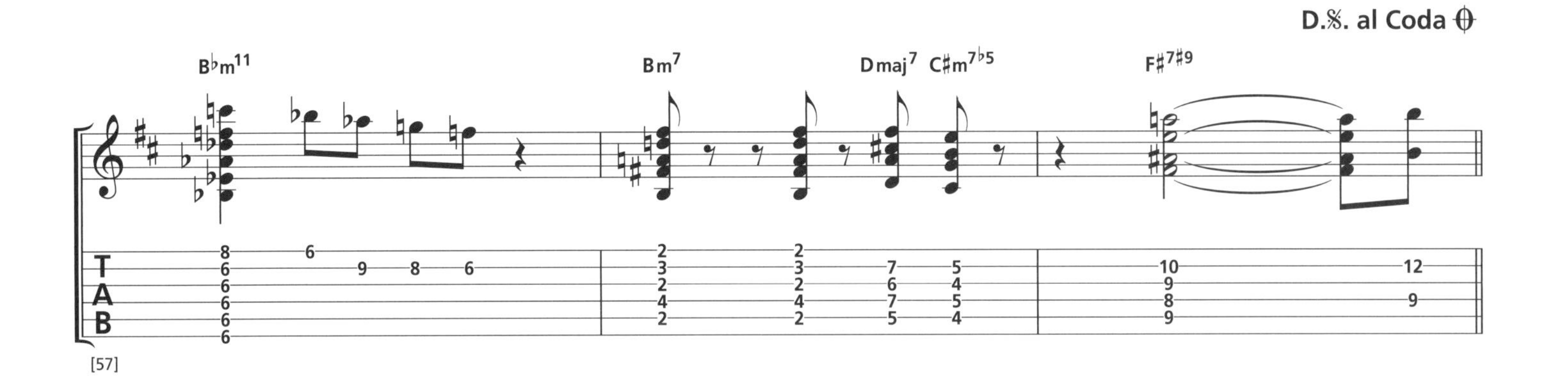
D.%. al Coda
B♭m11
Bm7
Dmaj7
C♯m7♭5
F♯7♯9
[57]

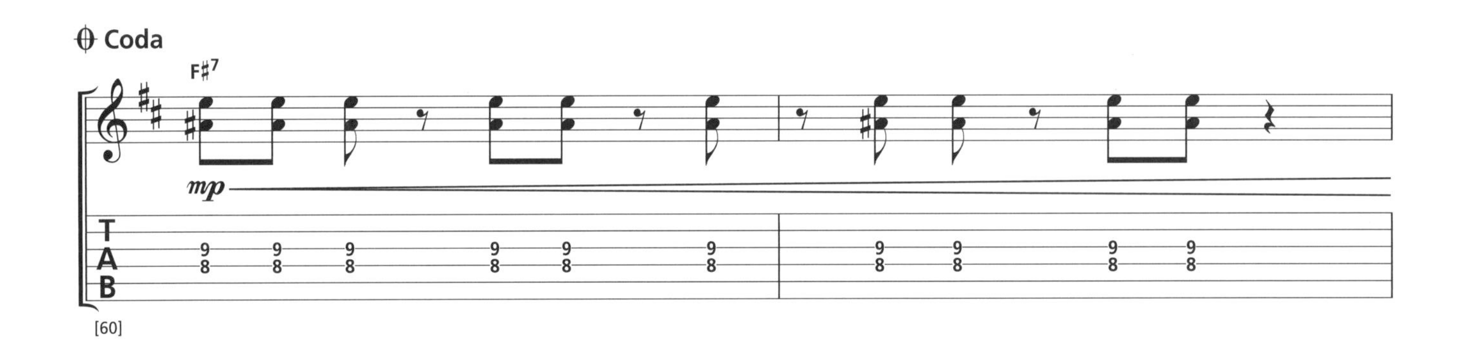
Coda
F♯7
mp
[60]

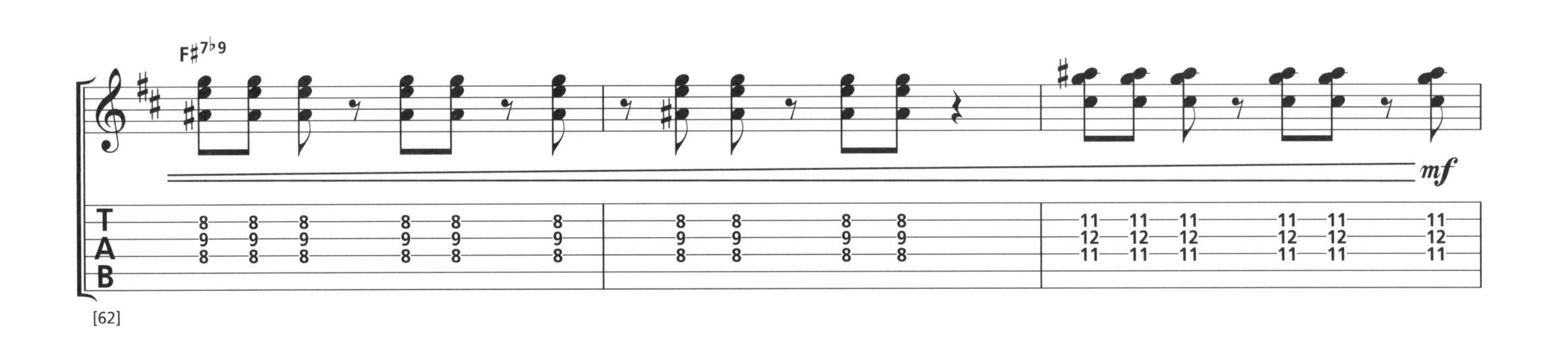
F♯7♭9
mf
[62]

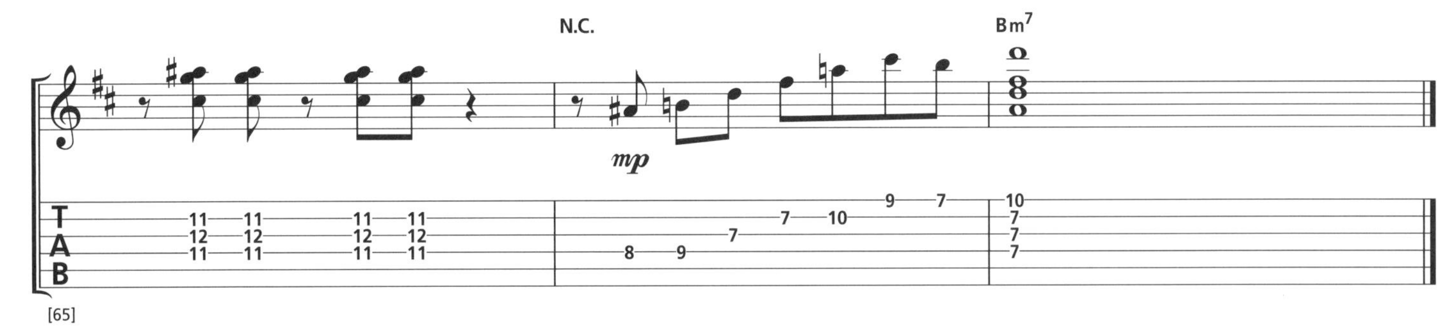
N.C.
Bm7
mp
[65]

Guitar Grade 7

Walkthrough

Amp Settings

Aim for a clean tone that's full and warm. Using your guitar's neck pickup will help with this. Boost the bass (but don't let the sound become too muddy) and roll off the middle and treble if you feel the sound is too harsh.

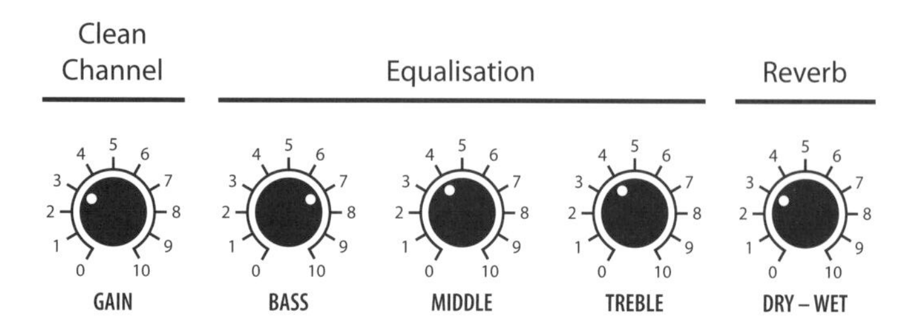

A Section (Bars 1–15)

The A section is a syncopated octave melody that utilises quick position shifts and slides.

Bars 1–67 | *Thumb or pick*
Although using the fleshy part of your thumb to play this piece will provide an authentic tone, it is quite challenging and not an exam requirement. You may find the best approach is play some sections with your thumb (i.e. accompanying the piano solo) and play the single note sections like bars 24–29 with a pick. No one approach is right or wrong; just ensure that your choices do not affect your performance.

Bars 1–15 | *Shifting and sliding octaves*
You should approach shifting and sliding octaves in the same way you would powerchords and barre chords: lock your fingers in position and move the fretting hand as a unit rather than dealing with individual finger placement. The added difficultly of sliding octaves is that you must maintain pressure on the strings to keep the notes ringing. You should feel as though you're pushing into the fretboard as well as sliding up or down to a new fret.

B Section (Bars 16–29)

The B section starts with strummed chords that are 'answered' by a single-note melodic phrase. This is followed by a chordal idea and a six-bar break where the guitar plays single-note lines based on various scales and arpeggios. It also makes use of grace notes, slides and hammer-ons.

Bars 16–21 | *Moving between chords and single notes*
Practise in two chord, one phrase sections so that you can rehearse moving from a chord to a melody and then to the next chord. Aim to place all of your fingers cleanly on the chord at the same time. When beginning this section, rehearse the movement from the chord to the first melody note repeatedly in isolation (Fig. 1).

C Section (Bars 30–53)

The C section is the guitar solo followed by the piano solo. Both are based in B minor.

Bars 30–41 | *Guitar solo*
The B dorian mode is an ideal choice for this solo. However, you will need to adjust your note choices over the F♯7 chord. The harmonic minor scale and dominant 7 arpeggio are two options. A more advanced approach, one commonly used in jazz, is to use the G melodic minor scale. This contains several of the notes found in the F♯ chord as well as the most common alterations (♭9, ♯9, etc), which creates an instantly jazzy sound (Fig. 2).

Bars 42–53 | *Piano solo*
You should create an accompaniment for the piano solo in this section. While you must create an interesting part, remember that your primary goal is to support the soloist.

D & E sections (Bars 54–67)

The D section further develops the chord/melody idea used in the B section. The E section is a reprise of the main melody followed by a rhythm that is repeated through several different chord voicings. This builds tension until the Bm7 chord provides a release.

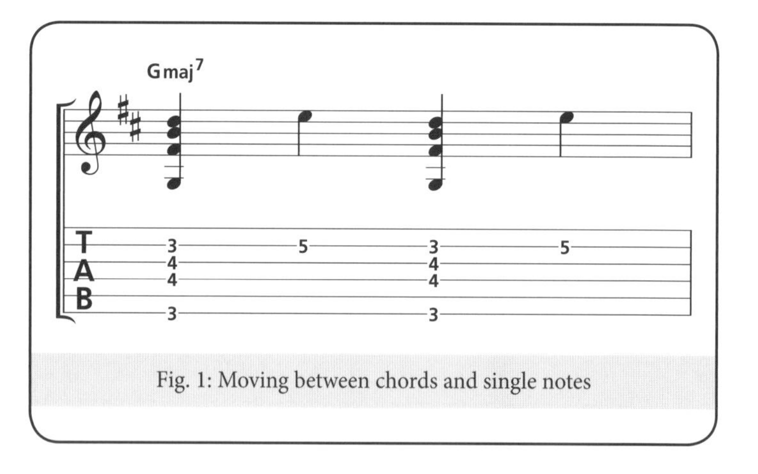

Fig. 1: Moving between chords and single notes

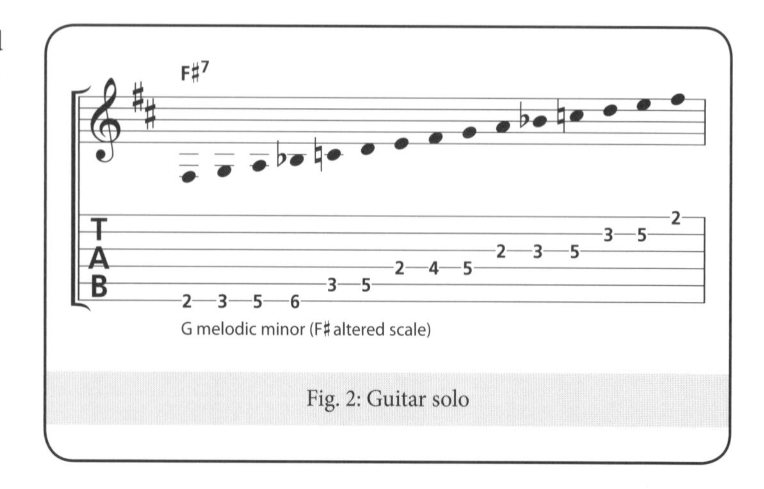

Fig. 2: Guitar solo

SONG TITLE: CHAOS PAD
GENRE: ROCK
TEMPO: 107 BPM
KEY: A MINOR

TECH FEATURES: ALTERNATE PICKING
MELODIC ROCK LINES
HARMONIC MINOR SCALE

COMPOSERS: JAMES UINGS
& DUNCAN JORDAN

PERSONNEL: STUART RYAN (GTR)
DAVE MARKS (BASS)
NOAM LEDERMAN (DRUMS)
DUNCAN JORDAN (KEYS)

OVERVIEW

'Chaos Pad' is a rock composition in the style of Devon rock power trio Muse. The main areas of influence that are evident within this song are a fast alternate picking riff on the fifth string using the open A note as a repeated pedal tone, as well as the use of notes drawn from the A harmonic minor scale – specifically the sound of the major 7th interval (G♯) in a minor context.

STYLE FOCUS

The harmonic minor scale is a classic rock guitar device that can be heard on many albums in the rock canon. Its popularity dates back to the 1970s and 1980s when it was favoured by bands and solo artists including Deep Purple and shred king Yngwie Malmsteen to create the neo-classical sound popular at the time.

Using an open string to create a repeating pedal tone is another staple technique of rock guitar. It can add the illusion of great complexity and technicality to riffs or solos that ascend or descend one string. With 'Chaos Pad' you would do well to note that you are alternate picking rather than deploying legato techniques (hammer-ons/pull-offs).

THE BIGGER PICTURE

Muse are one of the world's most successful contemporary power trios. Guitarist/frontman Matt Bellamy has a distinctive style that combines classic rock techniques with a modern player's sensibility and approach to riff writing. His guitar playing is often heavily processed and effects such as fuzz and pitch-shift have in part created the distinctive Muse sound. Bellamy will often contrast melodic lines with heavy riffs and his use of the harmonic minor scale adds the dark neo-classical sound to his writing. The band often use synth lines that give their music an industrial or prog flavour. Bellamy is considered a pioneer of the guitar, taking effects-laden six string sounds to new territories.

RECOMMENDED LISTENING

All five Muse studio albums showcase Bellamy's individual style. Their 1999 debut *Showbiz* is influenced by the alt rock sound of groups like Nirvana and Rage Against The Machine, and indie acts such Radiohead and Jeff Buckley. From their second album onwards, Muse incorporated more instruments, from strings to pipe organs. Their sound became heavier due to electronic and classic rock influences from Queen, Pink Floyd and others.

Chaos Pad

Tracks 7 & 8

James Uings & Duncan Jordan

D
N.C.
[16]
[18]
E
Am
G♯5
G5
F5
E5
Develop on repeat
BU BD
NH
[20]
[24]
Guitar Solo (16 bars)
C
D.%. al Coda
Play 4 times
[28]
Coda
PM
[32]

Guitar Grade 7

Walkthrough

Amp Settings

This heavier style of rock uses a modern high-gain distortion to create a smooth, saturated tone. The rhythm tone is not as scooped as a metal tone, but you may still wish to remove a little middle. However, boosting the middle in the solo will help the guitar cut through the dense mix.

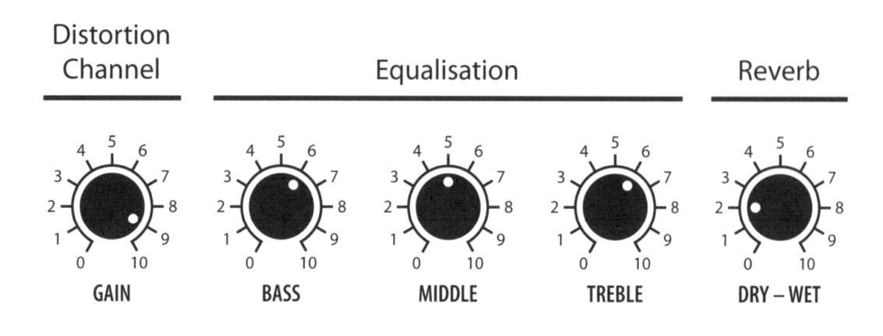

A Section (Bars 1–6)

The A section is a single-note melody that ascends the G string using slides and bends. It uses both the minor 7th (G) and major 7th (G♯).

Bars 1–5 | *Rhythmic accuracy*

A semi-tone bend from B to C happens four times in this section but two different rhythms are used. In the first rhythm the bend is played as a grace note, which means only the bent note has a note value. The actual bend is a quick note that precedes the target note (the note in brackets). In the second rhythm the un-bent note lasts for a 16th note, as does the target note. Make sure you observe these subtle rhythmic differences (Fig. 1).

B Section (Bars 7–10)

The B section is an intense alternate picked riff that uses the open A string as a pedal tone. The first half of the riff places the moving melody notes between two open A strings, while the second half places them between a single open A string.

Bars 7–10 | *Alternate picking*

These four bars are challenging and may require a fair amount of preparation on your part in order for you to play them up to speed while maintaining accuracy. Break the riffs down into two or four beat segments and work on them slowly. Maintain a relaxed picking motion with minimal movement and make sure that you fret cleanly. Fig. 2 clearly demonstrates how two-beat segments can be transferred into a picking exercise.

C & D Sections (Bars 11–19)

The C section is another intense riff and this time the pedal tones are fretted notes interspersed with hammer-ons and pull-offs. The D section is a repeat of the B section.

Bars 13–14 | *String skipping*

The most challenging part of this riff is bars 13 and 14, where you are required to skip over the D string. As a result, your pick has to travel considerably farther than it would if the notes were on adjacent strings without any extra time to make the jump. With this in mind, work to remove any excess motion in your picking action.

E Section (Bars 20–31)

The E section starts with a notated melody that you should develop on the repeat. The second part of the section is the guitar solo that is based in A minor.

Bars 20–27 | *Developing a part*

In these bars you should develop the part notated in bars 20–27. Common ways to develop a part are to vary the rhythm, note choices or articulations.

Bars 28–31 | *Guitar solo*

The guitar solo is 16 bars long. At 107 BPM this is quite a long time for you to improvise, so get a basic idea of the direction of your solo. Starting with slower, low register phrases before moving to more active licks in a higher register is just one way to give your solo shape.

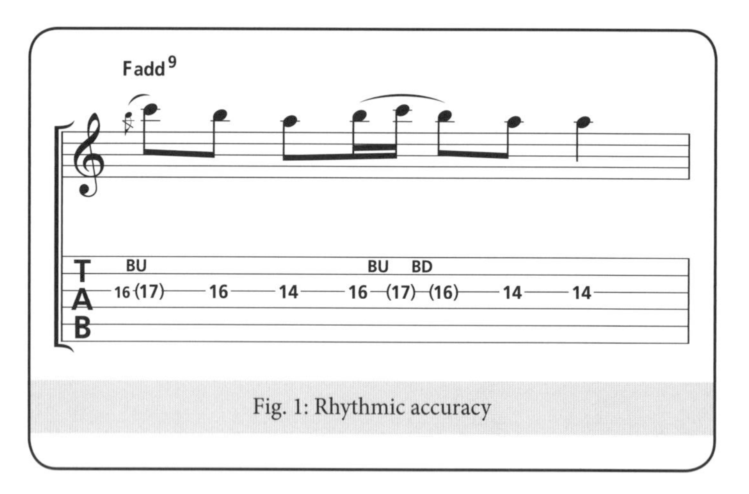

Fig. 1: Rhythmic accuracy

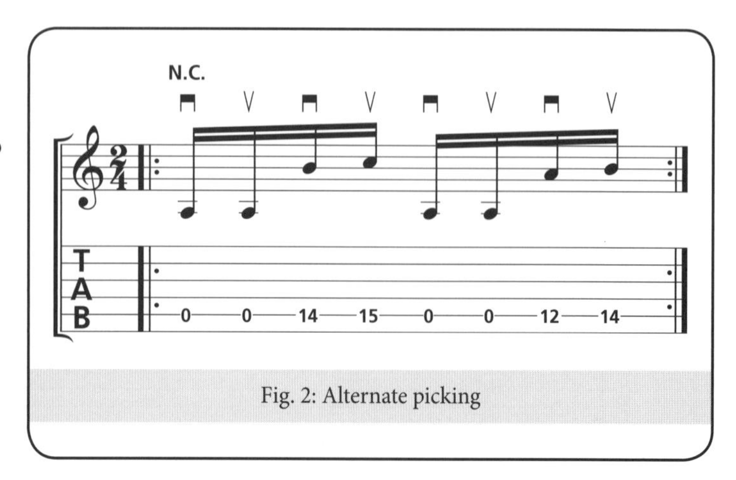

Fig. 2: Alternate picking

Natchez Trace

SONG TITLE: NATCHEZ TRACE
GENRE: COUNTRY
TEMPO: 105 BPM
KEY: A MAJOR

TECH FEATURES: HYBRID PICKING
OPEN-STRING LICKS
COUNTRY BENDS

COMPOSER: GLEN PARTRIDGE

PERSONNEL: KIT MORGAN (GTR)
HENRY THOMAS (BASS)
NOAM LEDERMAN (DRUMS)

OVERVIEW

'Natchez Trace' is a country guitar piece inspired by Albert Lee, Brad Paisley and Brent Mason. It features pedal steel style country bends, hybrid picking, string skipping and open-string licks among its techniques.

STYLE FOCUS

Country guitar can be challenging and players within this style use a number of tricks that may be new to you. A key element is hybrid picking. This involves plucking one string with your pick while playing another with the middle finger of your picking hand. This can take place on two adjacent strings or, more commonly, on non-adjacent strings (e.g. you might strike the low E string with your pick while playing the G string with your middle finger). A clean playing technique is essential because country players often use open strings that ring out against the other notes to emulate the sound of a banjo.

THE BIGGER PICTURE

Elvis and Gram Parsons sideman James Burton and singer Jerry Reed were two high profile guitarists who employed hybrid picking, pedal steel type bends and open string licks in their playing throughout the 1960s and 1970s. Both men were an influence on the English guitarist Albert Lee. Lee worked as a professional musician in the 1960s, but his big break came in 1976 when he was asked to replace his hero Burton in Emmylou Harris' band when the latter left to play once more with Elvis. Lee's signature tune 'Country Boy' was a hit for Ricky Skaggs in 1984.

After being discovered by country legend Chet Atkins in the early 1980s, Brent Mason became a sought-after session player famous for his hybrid picking and jazzy western swing influences. Mason has performed with country giants Alan Jackson, Brookes & Dunn and Shania Twain, and his first solo album *Hot Wired* was nominated for a Grammy.

Brad Paisley is a contemporary country star and a superb guitarist with a deft hybrid picking technique.

RECOMMENDED LISTENING

To hear Lee's playing style, listen to Emmylou Harris' 1977 album *Luxury Liner*. Mason's first solo album, *Hot Wired* (1997), combines the guitarist's country and jazz influences. Paisley's 2008 *Play* features 'Cluster Pluck' and includes performances by Burton, Lee, Vince Gill and John Jorgensen.

Natchez Trace

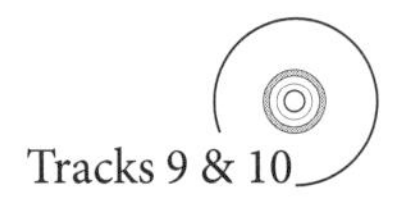

Glen Partridge

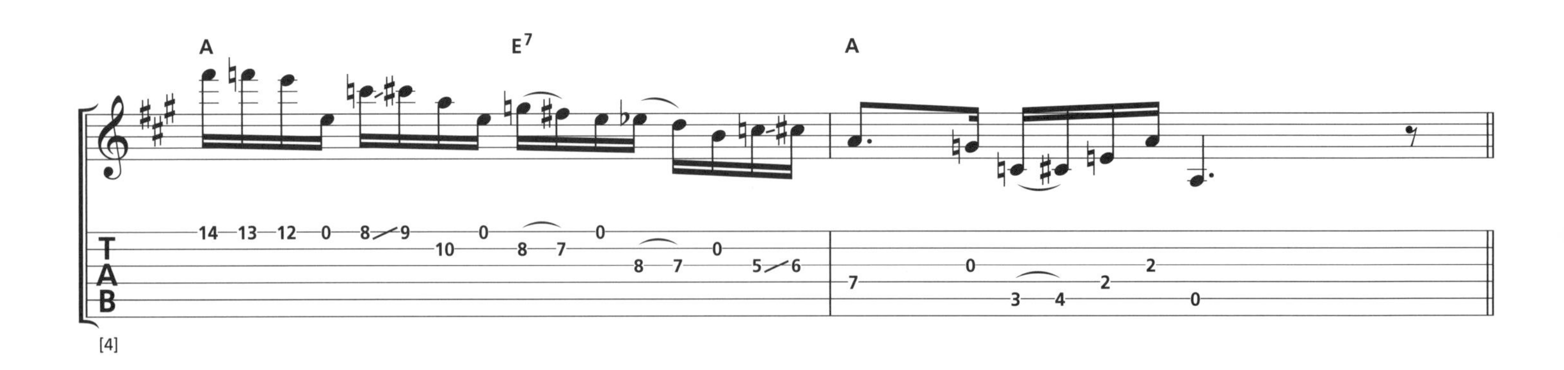

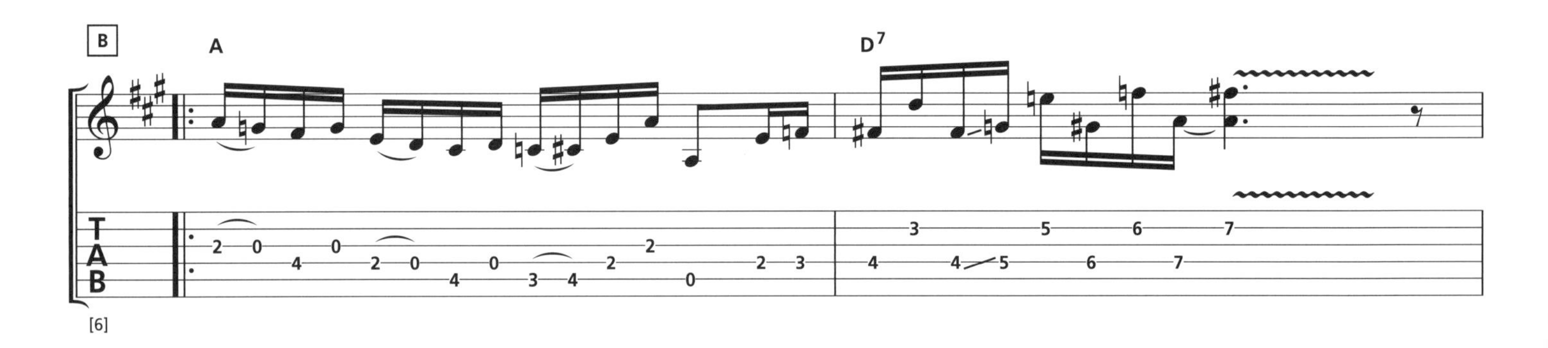

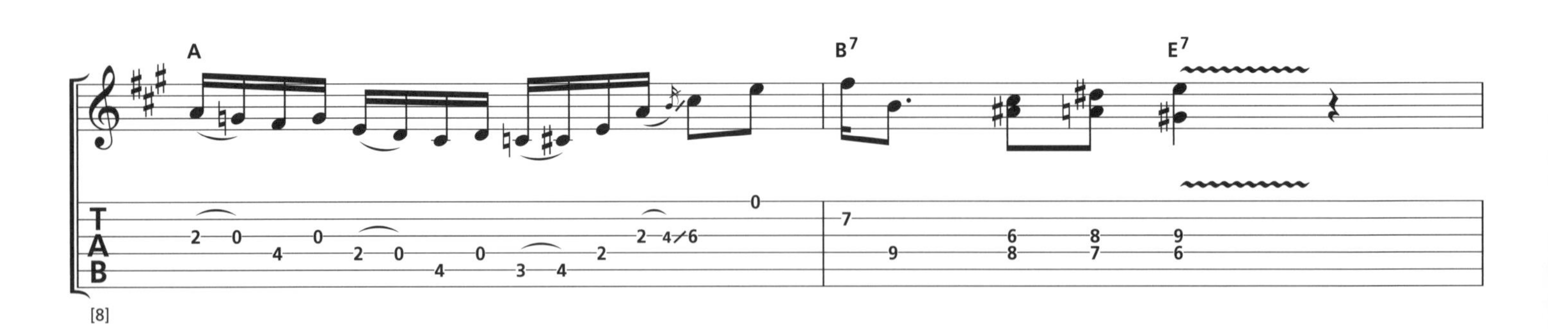

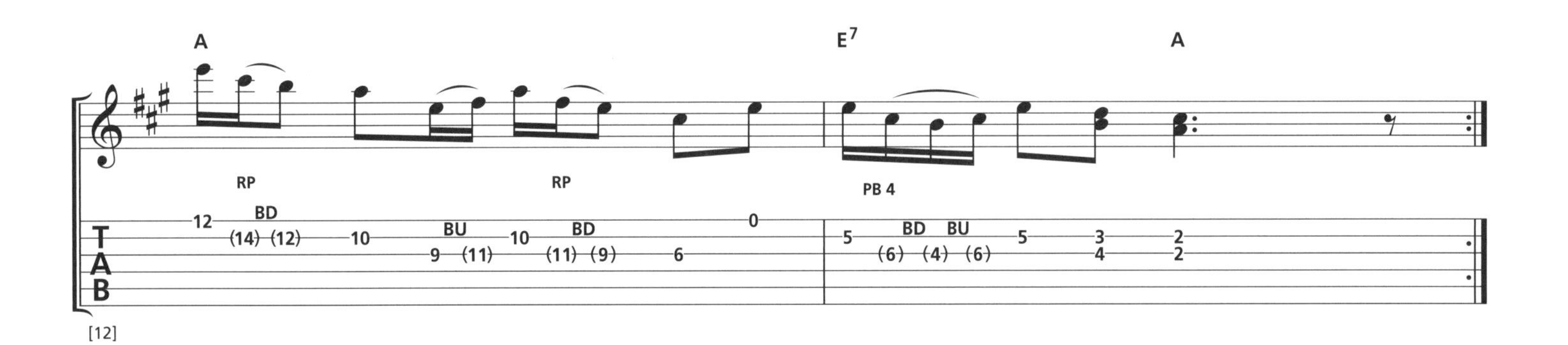
A
E7
A
RP
RP
PB 4
BD
BU
BD
BD
BU
TAB
[12]

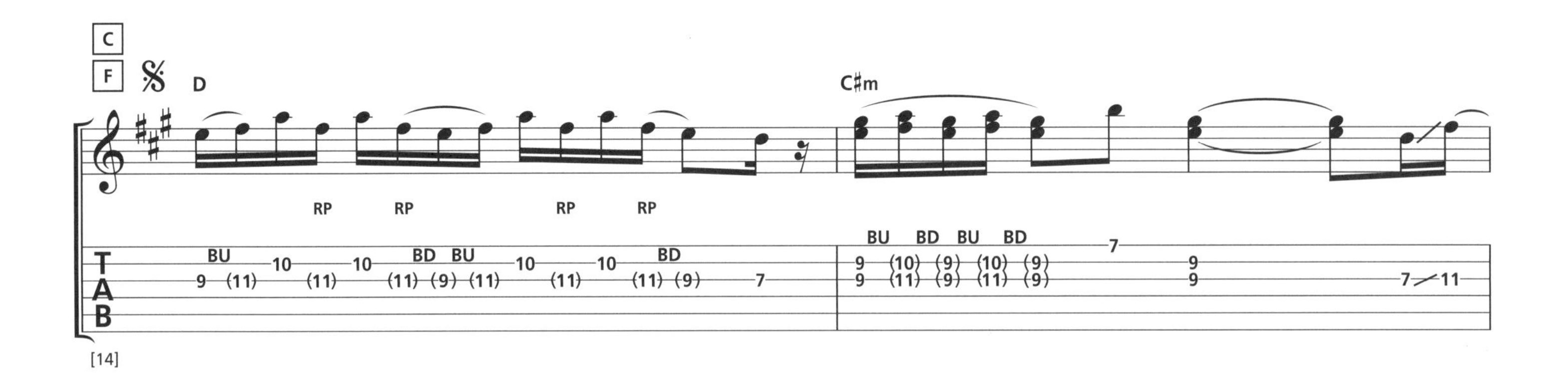
C
F
D
C♯m
RP
RP
RP
RP
BU
BD
BU
BD
BU
BD
BU
BD
TAB
[14]

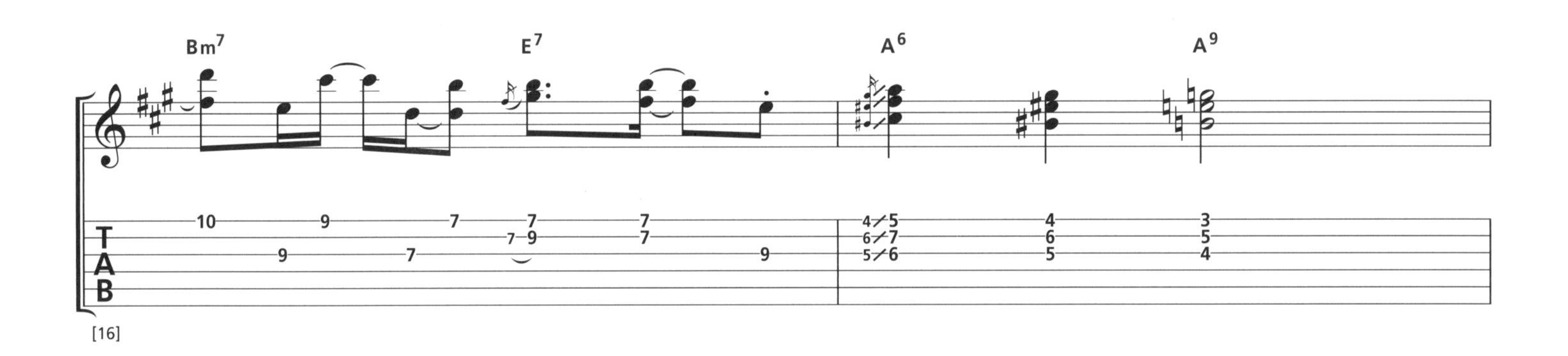
Bm7
E7
A6
A9
TAB
[16]

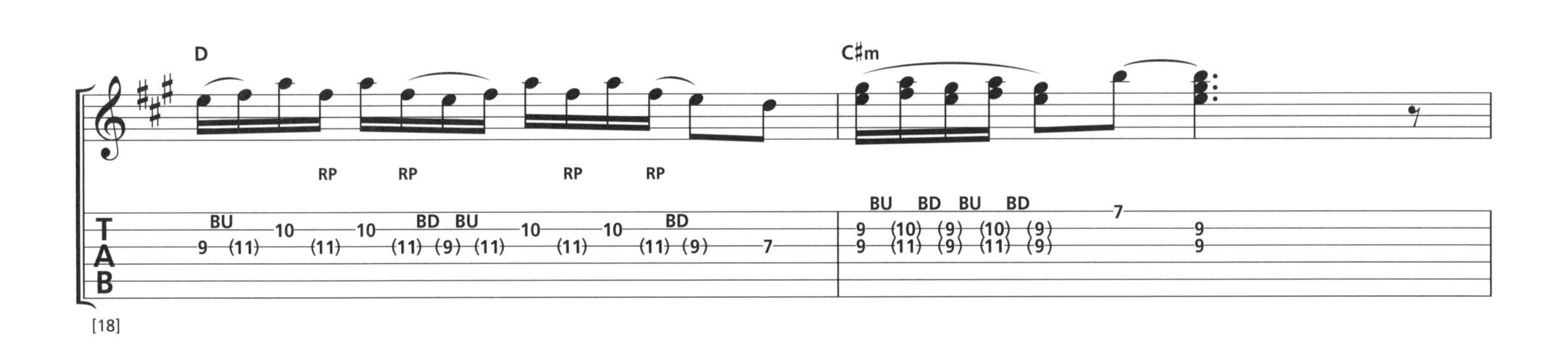
D
C♯m
RP
RP
RP
RP
BU
BD
BU
BD
BU
BD
BU
BD
TAB
[18]

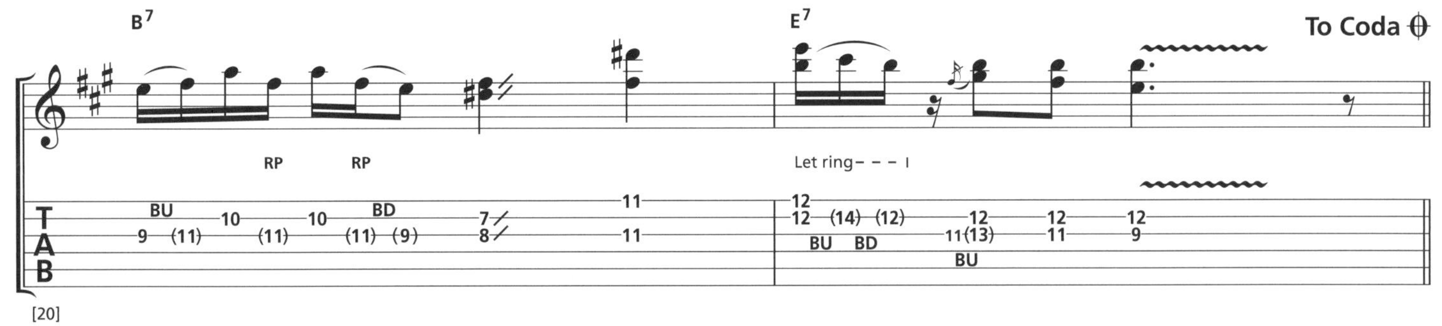
B7
E7
To Coda
RP
RP
Let ring
BU
BD
BU
BD
BU
TAB
[20]

Guitar Grade 7

Western Swing
D
G♯13 A13 G♯13 A13 G♯13 A13 G♯13 A13 G♯13 A13 C♯9 D9 C♯9 D9 C♯9 D9 C♯9 D9 C♯9 D9 G♯13
[22]
A13 A6/9 A6 B13 B7♯5♭9 E9 E7♯5♭9
[24]
A6/9 A7♯5 D9 E♭dim
8va
[26]
E
E7 E7 A
[28]
Guitar Solo (16 bars)
A D7 A B7 E7
[30]
D.%. al Coda
A A7 D E♭dim A E7 A
(Solo through)
[34]

Coda
A
D7
TAB
[38]

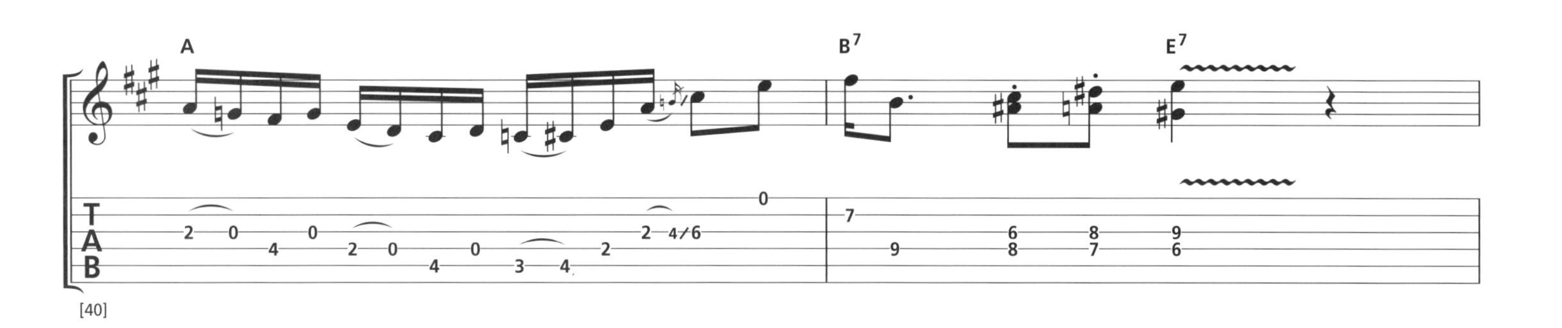
A
B7
E7
TAB
[40]

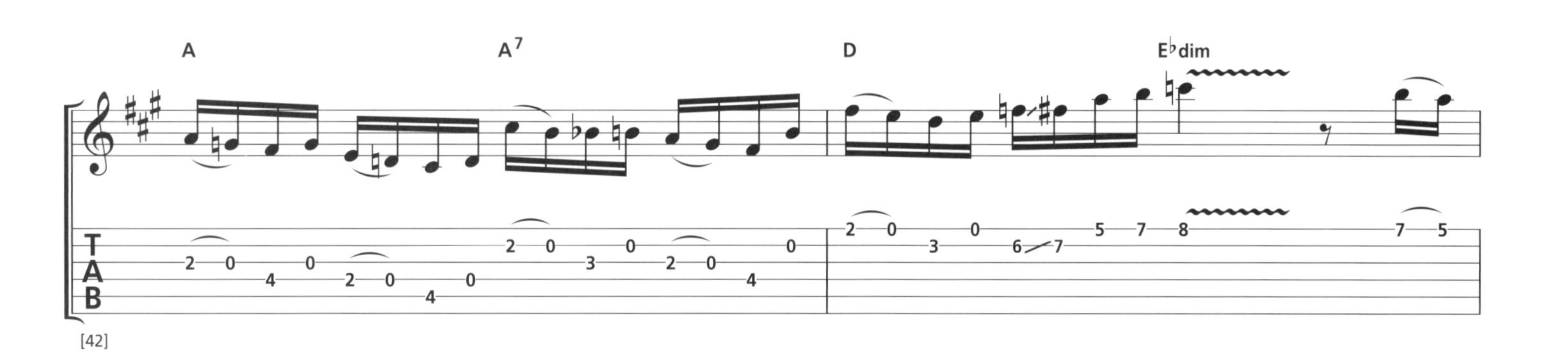
A
A7
D
E♭dim
TAB
[42]

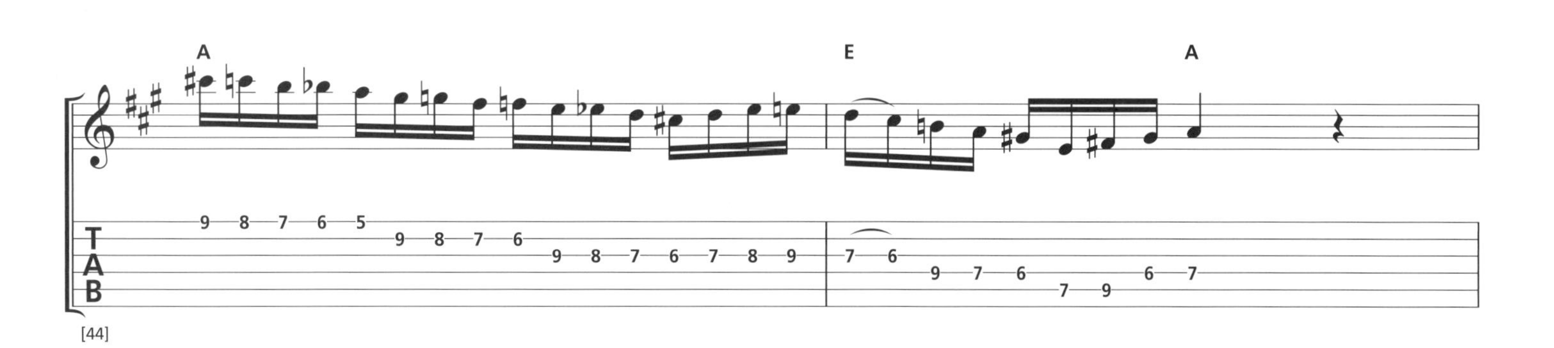
A
E
A
TAB
[44]

Adim
Cdim
E7
A
TAB
[46]

Walkthrough

Amp Settings

Work with a clean, bright tone and generous reverb. Use your guitar's bridge pickup to help get the brightest tone and give your phrases some snap, but boost the treble and middle if you still feel your tone is missing a little edge.

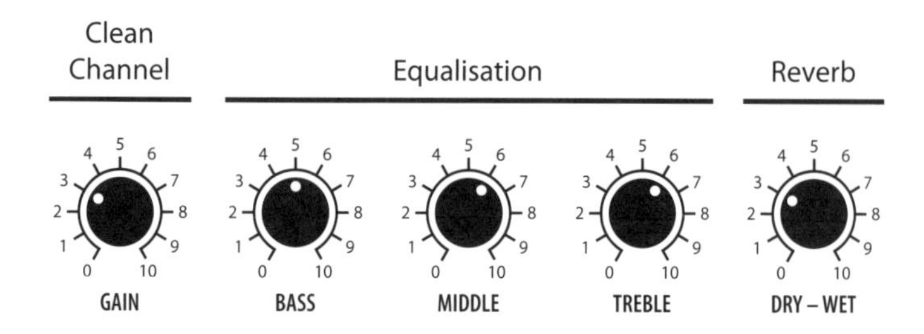

A Section (Bars 1–5)

The A section is a single-note line that is full of chromatic notes. Slides, hammer-ons and pull-offs are used to give notes a smooth, slippery feel. Allow open strings to ring on to further enhance the flowing feel.

Bars 1–3 | *Hybrid picking*
Hold the pick between your thumb and index finger. Pick the G string and pluck the E string with your ring finger at the same time. It should strike the string at a slight diagonal, moving up towards the heel of the thumb. Use your pick or hybrid picking for the remainder of the phrase. (Fig. 1).

B Section (Bars 6–13)

This classic country melody uses open strings, double-stops and re-picked bends. The 6th interval is used extensively.

Bars 6–13 | *Consistent hammer-ons and pull-offs*
Avoid rushing hammer-ons and pull-offs, otherwise the first note won't sound for the correct amount of time.

C Section (Bars 14–21)

This is based primarily on different types of string bends.

Bar 15 | *Double-stop bends*
This double-stop bend should be played with your third finger on both frets supported by your first and second fingers (Fig. 2). As you push or pull the string, make sure you maintain pressure *into* the fretboard to keep the note ringing for the duration of the bend.

Bar 21 | *Oblique bends*
An oblique bend is a string bend played simultaneously with at least one un-bent note. Play the bend in beat one with your third finger supported by the first and second fingers while playing the E at the 12th fret with your fourth finger. Use the same fingering for the lick in beat two.

D Section (Bars 22–27)

Here the piece moves to a swing feel. Extended chord shapes are used to give the section its western swing feel.

Bars 22–27 | *Fast chord changes*
Although it may appear complex, each bar is made up of a single chord shape shifted up and down a semitone. Lock your hand in position and move your whole hand rather than individual fingers.

E & F Sections (Bars 28–47)

The E section is the guitar solo, while the F section is a reprise of the C and B sections. The final four bars consist of a chromatic run that is followed by two diminished arpeggios then an open string lick that leads to the last chord of the piece.

Bars 30–37 | *Guitar solo*
It is a common mistake for soloists to look for something new to play in *every* bar. Usually, the most well-constructed, memorable solos will have at least one element that is repeated even if it is just a rhythm or melodic hook. Bear this in mind here.

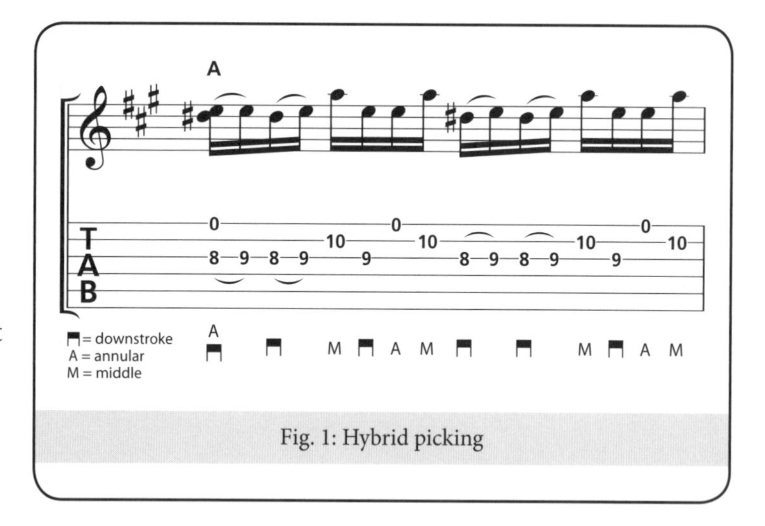

Fig. 1: Hybrid picking

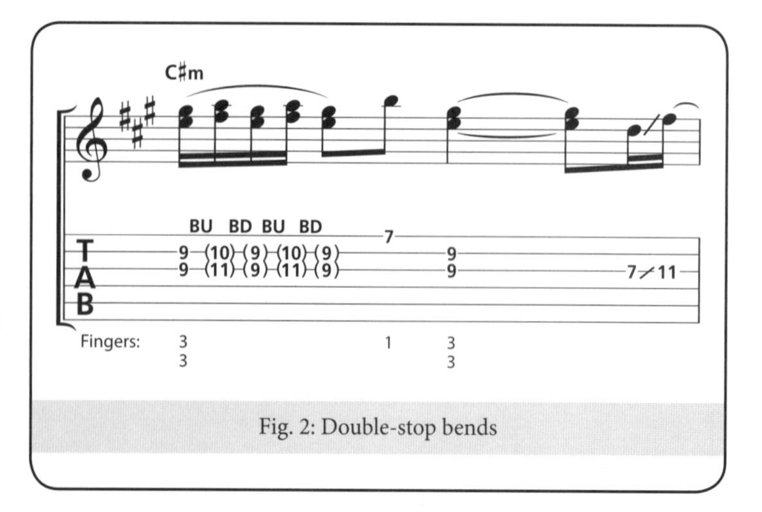

Fig. 2: Double-stop bends

Times Square

SONG TITLE: TIMES SQUARE
GENRE: JAZZ FUNK
TEMPO: 87 BPM
KEY: G MINOR

TECH FEATURES: DOUBLE-STOP MELODIES
WIDE INTERVALS
CHROMATIC RUNS

COMPOSER: KIT MORGAN

PERSONNEL: KIT MORGAN (GTR)
HENRY THOMAS (BASS)
NOAM LEDERMAN (DRUMS)
ROSS STANLEY (KEYS)
CARL STERLING (SAX)

OVERVIEW

'Times Square' is a jazz funk piece comprised of a tight groove and a guitar melody played in double-stops that must be performed with clean phrasing and accurate timing. You will also find other characteristic devices, such as palm muted single-note rhythm figures and a more advanced harmony in several of the licks. Listen out for the contrast in clean and overdriven guitar tones too.

STYLE FOCUS

This particular strain of jazz funk melds sophisticated jazz harmony and phrasing with tight funky grooves. It is a slick sound that is often associated with session players Larry Carlton and Lee Ritenour, and sax giant Michael Brecker. One of the most prominent jazz funk guitarists is John Scofield, who developed the style during his days as sideman to the legendary jazz trumpeter Miles Davis and later, on recordings as a leader in his own right.

THE BIGGER PICTURE

Jazz funk emerged in the late 1960s when band leaders like Davis used funk's static harmony as a base on which to improvise. Later musicians began to introduce complex jazz harmony in catchy ways and the music developed an appeal beyond an audience of musicians or those loyal to the individual genres of jazz and funk.

There is an aspect of jazz funk known as smooth jazz, which typically features a softer sound and simpler harmony. This smoother form grew out of the disco, soul and pop sounds of the 1970s and 1980s as the session musicians who played on classic pop albums began composing their own music using the sensibilities they learned on major recording sessions. Level 42 had success with this style by marrying vocals with jazz funk grooves. For guitarists, a common rhythmic device is to play two palm-muted notes consecutively with a 16th-note rhythm (you will hear this demonstrated on 'Times Square').

RECOMMENDED LISTENING

Rit (1981) by session supremo Lee Ritenour is a lesson in smooth jazz funk guitar. His friend and contemporary Larry Carlton is also a master of this style, and his album *Larry Carlton* (1978) features the track 'Room 335', a classic of this genre. For a harder edge try John Scofield's *Blue Matter* (1986) or Mike Stern's *Upside Downside* (1986).

Times Square

Tracks 11 & 12

Kit Morgan

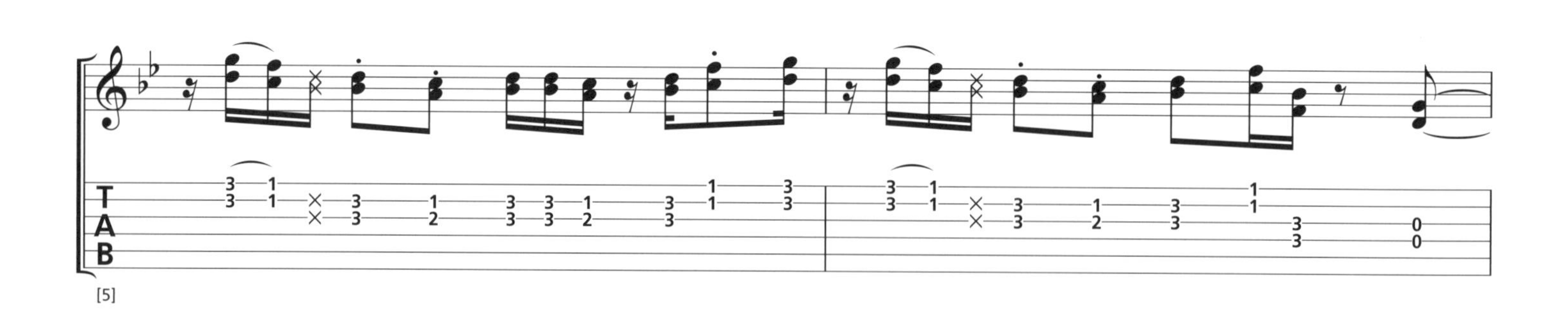

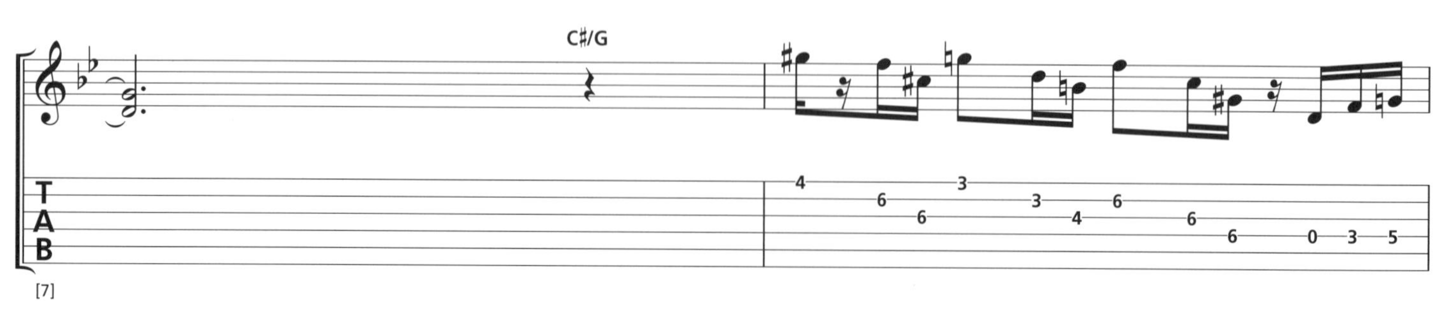

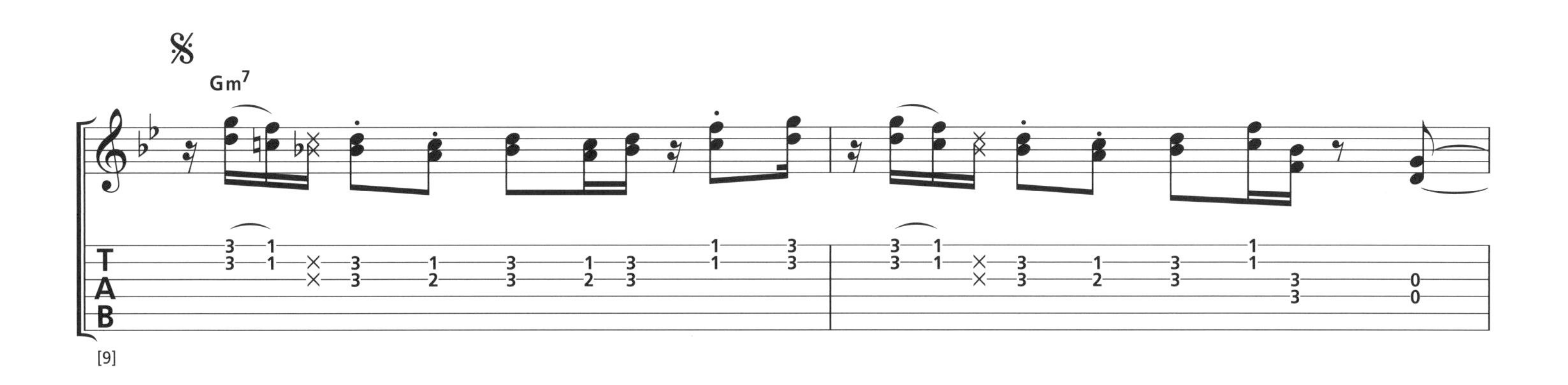
Gm7
T
A
B
[9]

Fill on 𝄋
PM
1/4
1/4
T
A
B
[11]

Gm7
T
A
B
[13]

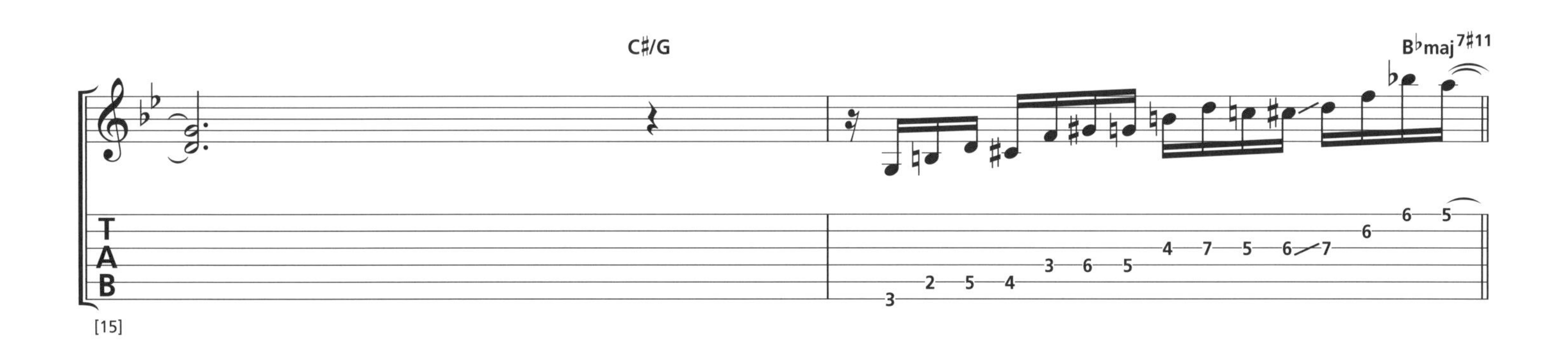
C♯/G
B♭maj7♯11
T
A
B
[15]

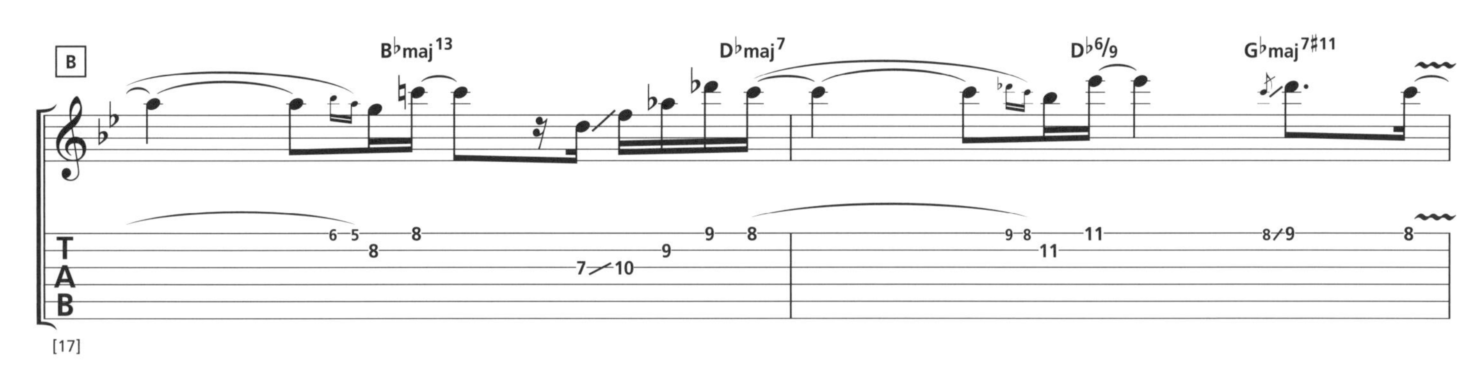
B
B♭maj13
D♭maj7
D♭6/9
G♭maj7♯11
T
A
B
[17]

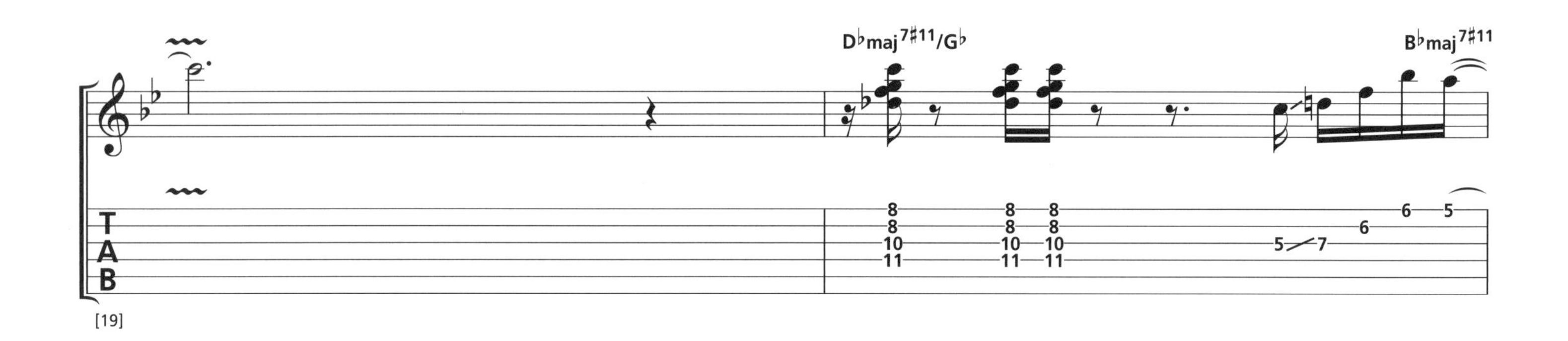
D♭maj7♯11/G♭
B♭maj7♯11
T
A
B
[19]

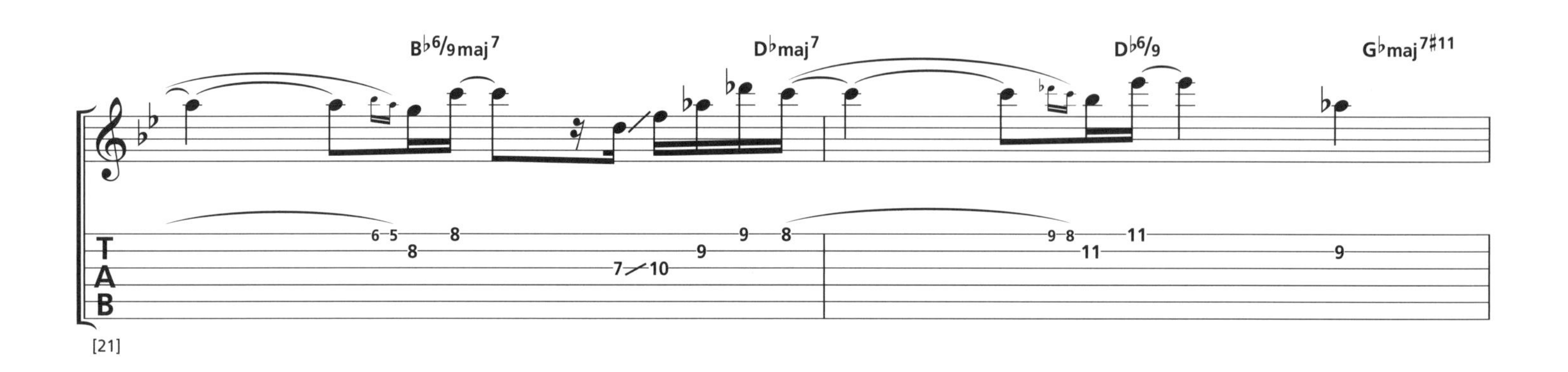
B♭6/9maj7
D♭maj7
D♭6/9
G♭maj7♯11
T
A
B
[21]

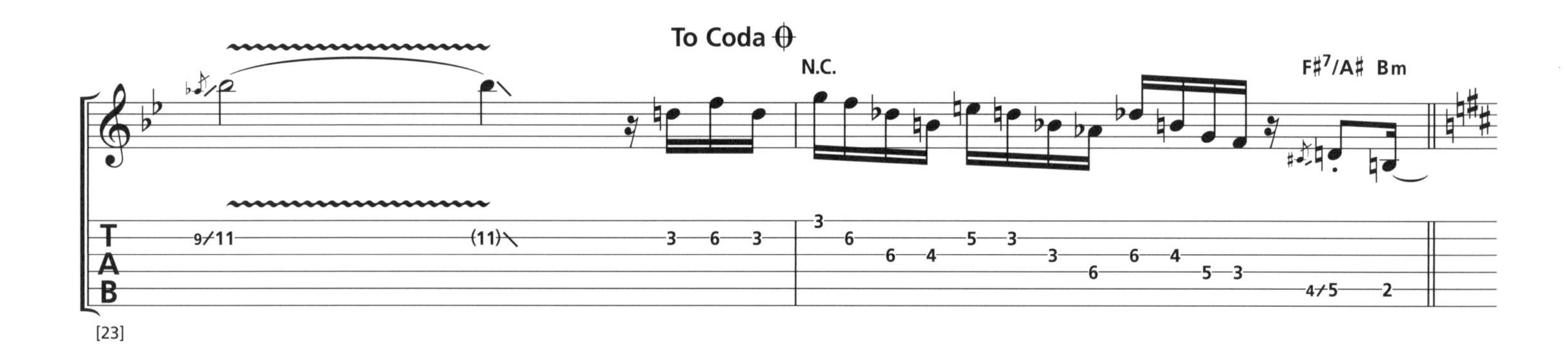
To Coda
N.C.
F♯7/A♯
Bm
T
A
B
[23]

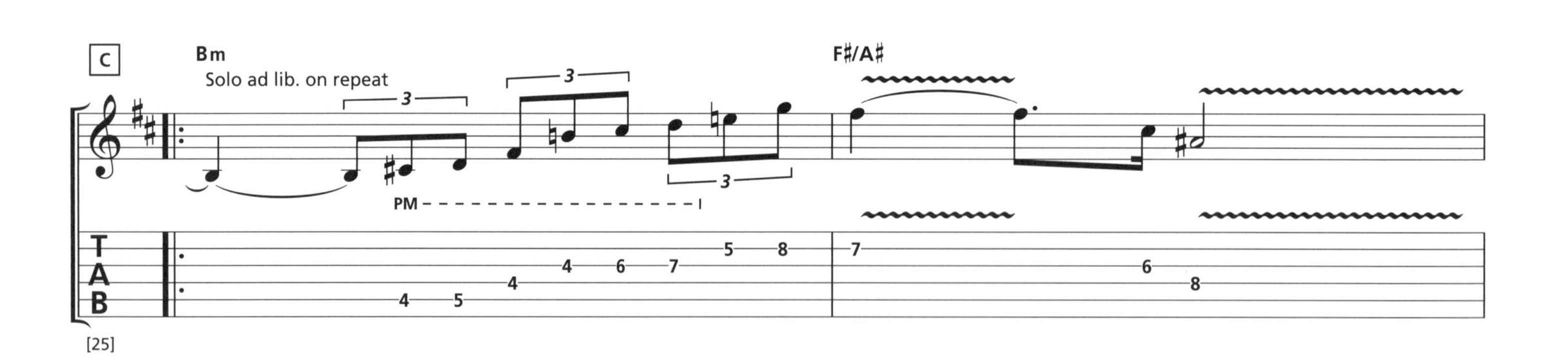
C
Bm
Solo ad lib. on repeat
F♯/A♯
PM
T
A
B
[25]

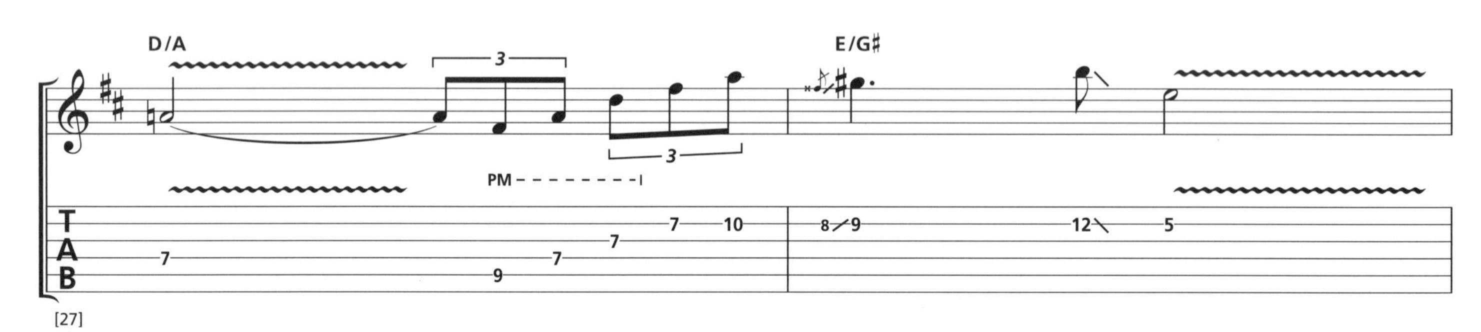
D/A
E/G♯
PM
T
A
B
[27]

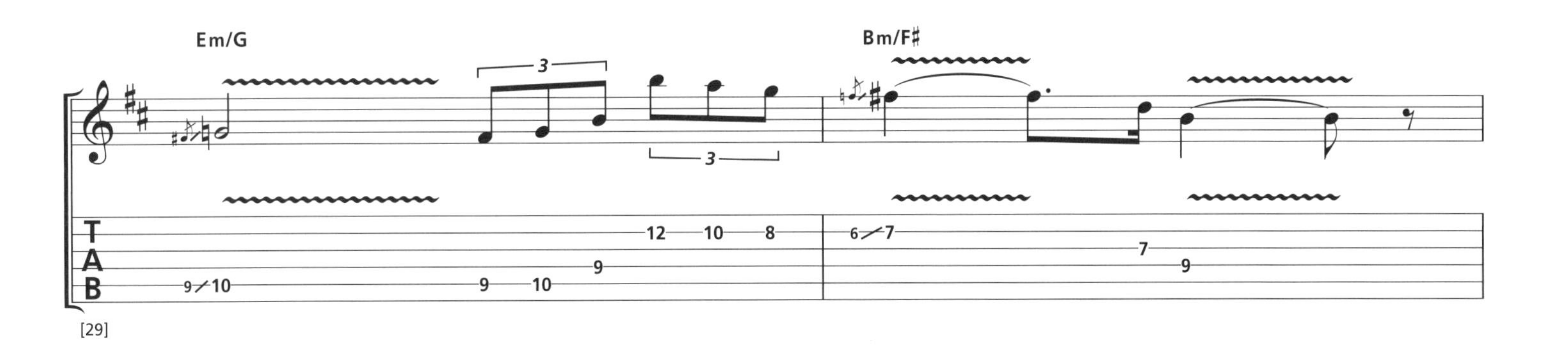
Em/G
Bm/F♯
TAB
[29]

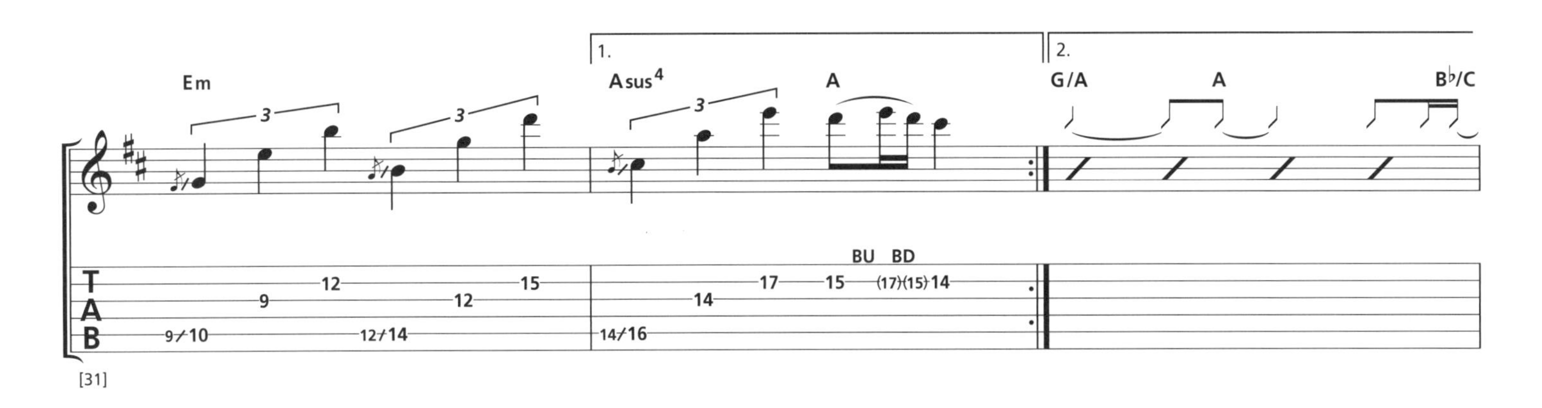
Em
1.
Asus4
A
2.
G/A
A
B♭/C
BU BD
TAB
[31]

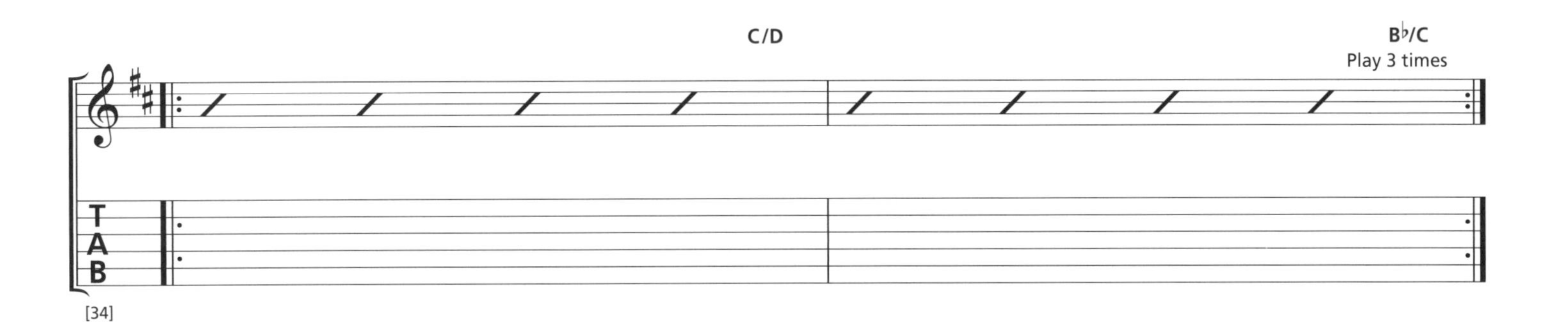
C/D
B♭/C
Play 3 times
TAB
[34]

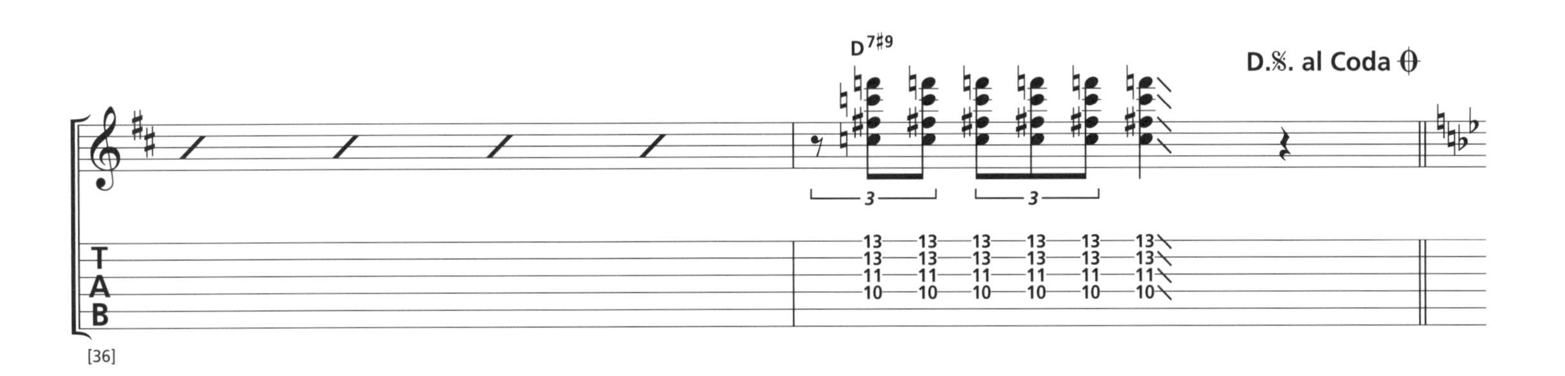
D7♯9
D.𝄋. al Coda
TAB
[36]

Coda
N.C.
F7♯9
F♯7♯9
G7♯9
TAB
[38]

Guitar Grade 7

Walkthrough

Amp Settings

The tone you will need to complement the funky riffs found in 'Times Square' is bright and clean. The distorted tone should be fairly overdriven, so choose a smooth sound that maintains its clarity. Make sure the balance between the two tones is correct. Remember, clean tones are slightly quieter than distorted tones.

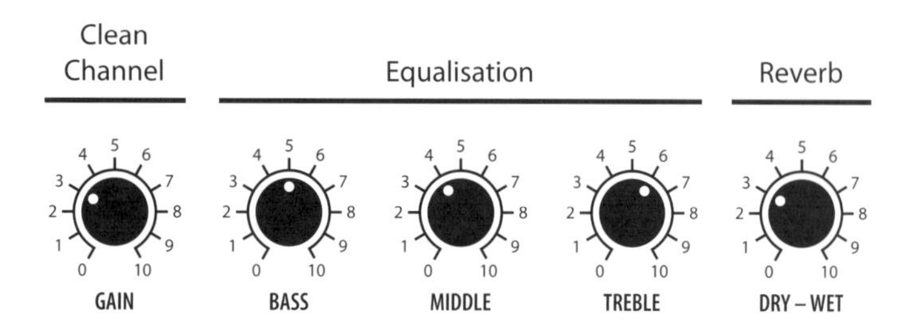

A Section (Bars 1–16)

The A section consists of a funky three-bar, double-stop riff that is answered by single-note phrases.

Bars 1–2 | *Ghost strumming*
Keeping your hand in a constant strumming motion will help you play the syncopated rhythms, particularly the first note that starts on an upbeat. When you don't want to strike the strings, move your pick a small amount away from the them (these are called ghost strums).

Bar 8 | *Finger rolls*
When two or more notes follow each other on the same fret but on different strings (there are many in this track) you must roll your finger to prevent the notes from bleeding into each other. Play the first note with the pad of your finger and the second note by rolling onto the tip of your finger by bending it at the first knuckle. If there are more than two notes, the first note should be played with a lower part of the pad just above your first knuckle.

B Section (Bars 17–24)

The B section actually starts in the last bar of the A section with a jazzy run that ends on the first note of the melody. The B section melody is flowing and makes use of fast embellishments

Bars 17–22 | *Multiple grace notes*
These two grace notes should be played quickly just before the main melody notes in beat two. Use a flicking motion to produce the flurry of notes you are looking for.

Bars 23–24 | *Descending run*
This tricky run breaks down into manageable one-beat chunks that can be rehearsed as an exercise until you feel you are ready to connect them into one long phrase (Fig. 1).

C Section (Bars 25–36)

The C section melody contrasts ascending runs with sustained chord tones. The first half of the section ends with a wide interval lick. Start your guitar solo on the repeat; the solo continues through the second time bar.

Bars 31–32 | *Wide intervals*
This lick is awkward because you have to shift your hand quickly after each sequence of three notes. Play the first note of each group with your second finger.

Bars 25–36 | *Guitar solo*
The guitar solo features a challenging sequence to solo over because you will have to make adjustments to your scale/arpeggio choices every few bars. There are countless options, so what follows are only suggestions. The first four bars could be thought of as E dorian with an adjustment needed for the F♯/A♯ chord. Either change the A notes to A♯ notes, use the harmonic minor or base your lines on the F♯ arpeggio. The natural minor scale will work for the next four bars. Many jazz guitarists will think of the B♭/C (C, B♭, D & F) as a C^{11} chord (Fig. 2) and consequently use the C mixolydian mode. G/A and C/D are the same chord transposed and can be treated in the same way.

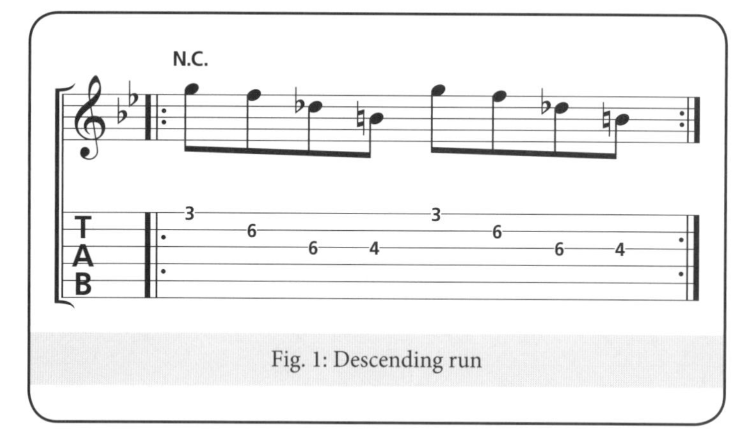

Fig. 1: Descending run

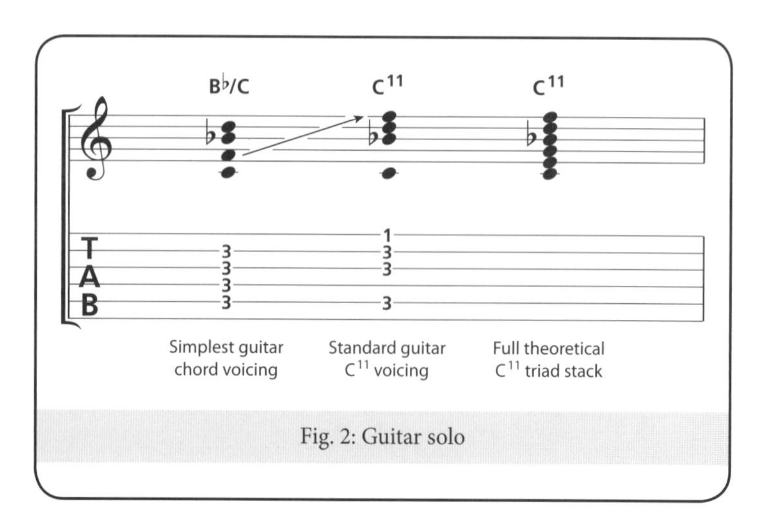

Fig. 2: Guitar solo

Technical Exercises

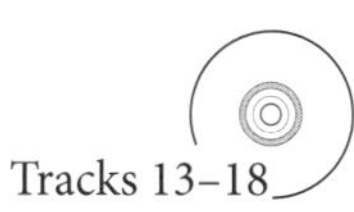

Tracks 13–18

In this section the examiner will ask you to play a selection of exercises drawn from each of the four groups shown below. Groups A, B and C contain examples of the scales and modes, arpeggios and chords you can use when playing the pieces. In Group D you will be asked to prepare *one* stylistic study from the three printed. The choice of stylistic study will determine the style of the Quick Study Piece.

You do not need to memorise the exercises (and can use the book in the exam) but the examiner will be looking for the speed of your response. The examiner will also give credit for the level of your musicality.

Before you start the section you will be asked whether you would like to play the exercises along with the click or hear a single bar of click before you commence the test. The tempo is ♩= 100.

Group A: Scales and Modes

Two octaves, two positions. The first position is to be prepared on the E string from the starting notes of G–B chromatically. The second position is to be prepared on the A string from the starting notes of C–E chromatically.

1. Lydian (G lydian shown, root on E string)

2. Phrygian (B phrygian shown, root on E string)

3. Jazz melodic minor (C jazz melodic minor shown, root on A string)

Group B: Arpeggios

One octave, two positions. The first position is to be prepared on the E string from the starting notes of G–B chromatically. The second position is to be prepared on the A string from the starting notes of C–E chromatically.

1. Major⁹ arpeggios (A major⁹ arpeggio shown, root on E string)

2. Minor^9 arpeggios (B minor^9 arpeggio shown, root on A string)

3. Dominant^9 arpeggios (D^9 arpeggio shown, root on A string)

Group C: Chords

Two positions. The first position is to be prepared on the E string from the starting notes of G–B chromatically. The second position is to be prepared on the A string from the starting notes of C–E chromatically. Chords should be strummed and then picked (arpeggiated).

1. Major^9 chords (A major^9 chord shown, root on E string)

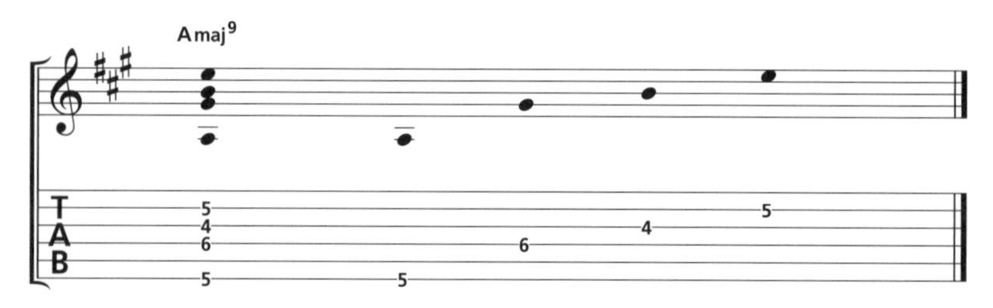

2. Minor^9 chords (B minor^9 chord shown, root on A string)

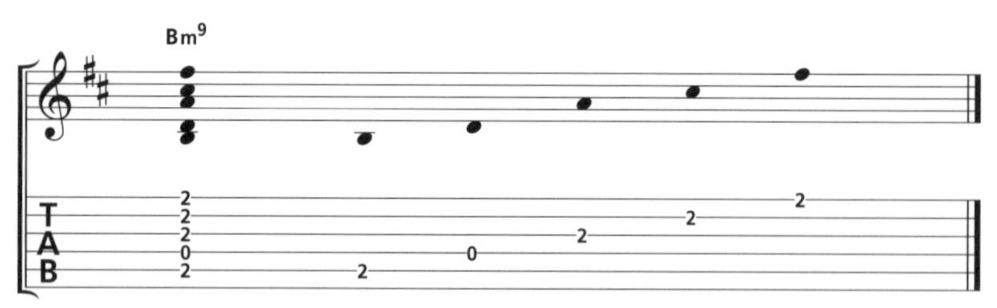

3. Dominant^9 chords (D^9 chord shown, root on A string)

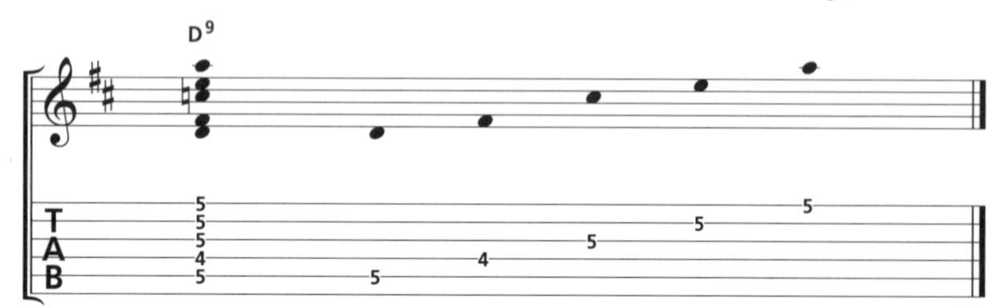

Group D: Stylistic Studies

You will prepare a technical study from one group of styles from the list below. Your choice of style will determine the style of the Quick Study Piece.

1. Rock/Metal: pinch harmonics and natural harmonics

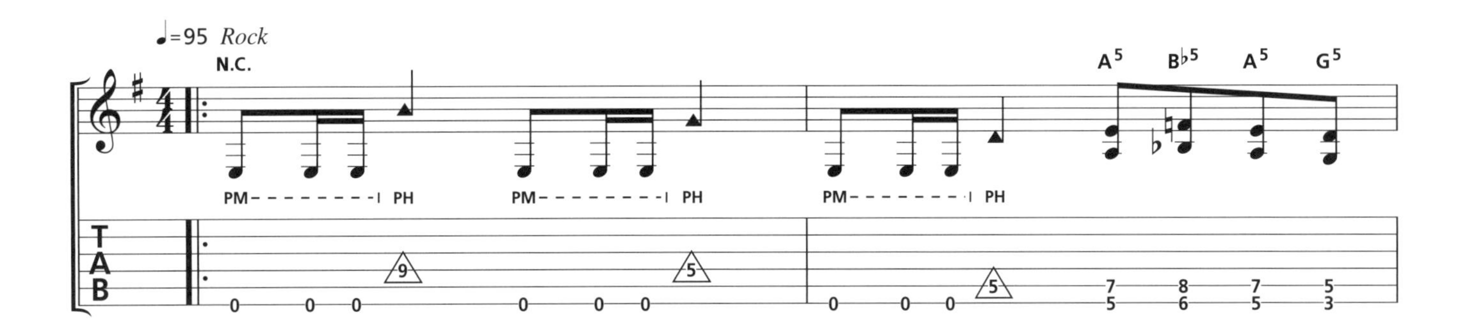

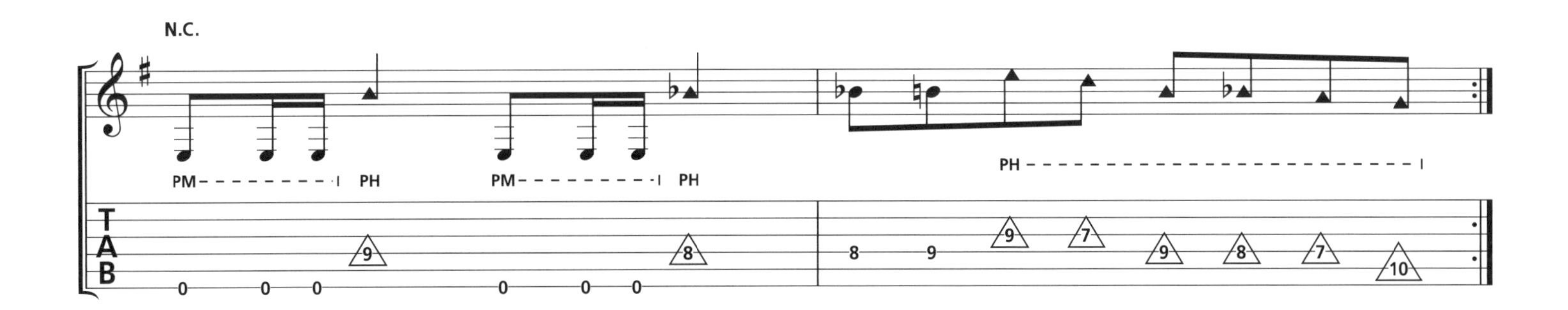

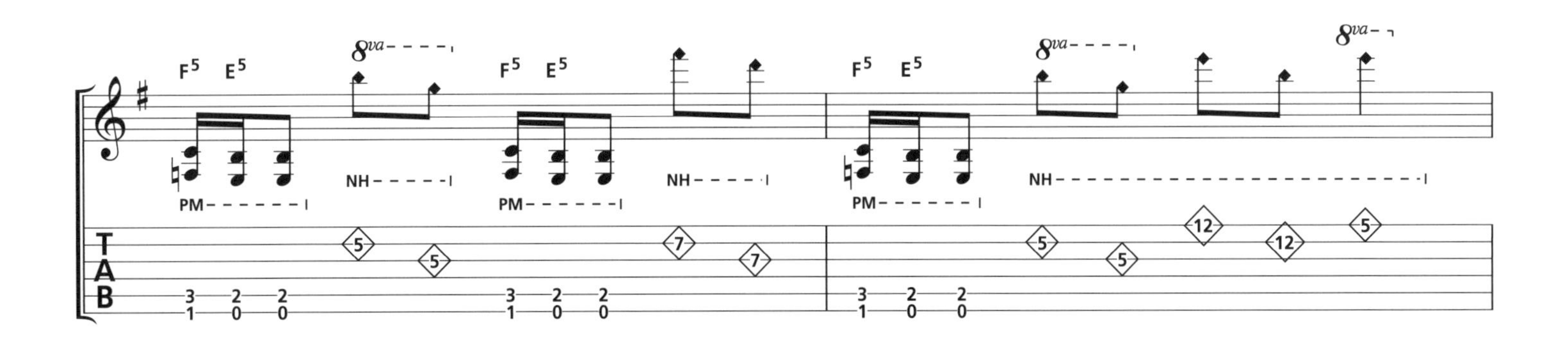

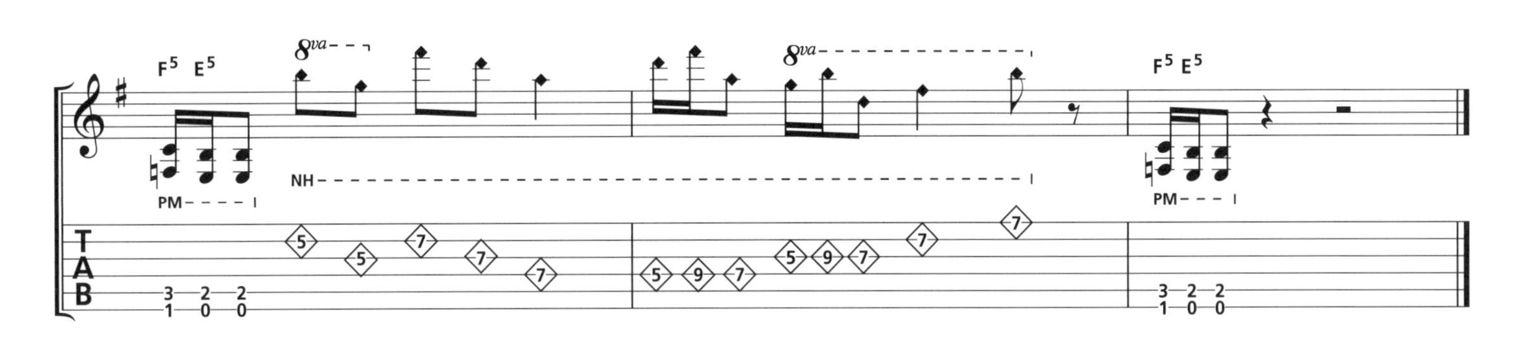

2. Funk: chordal embellishments and double-stops

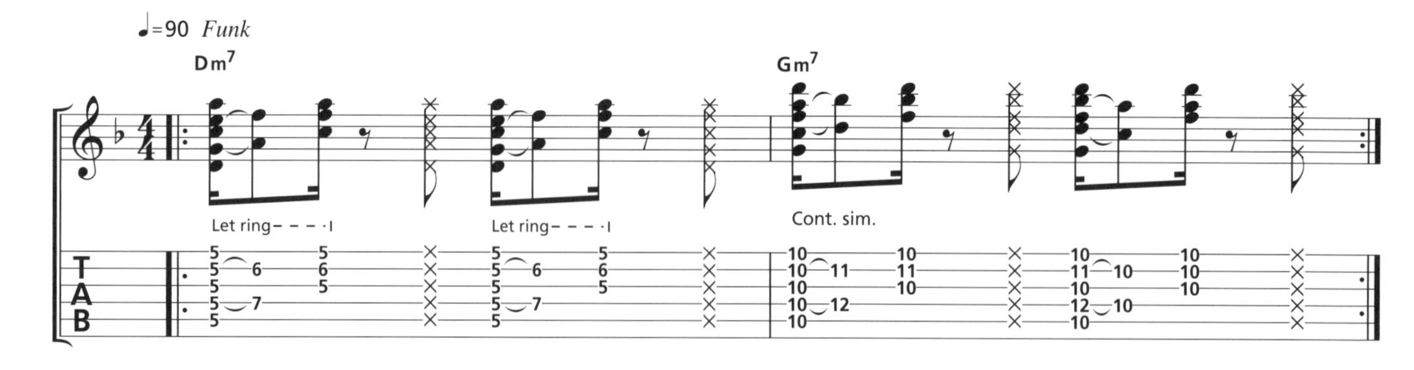

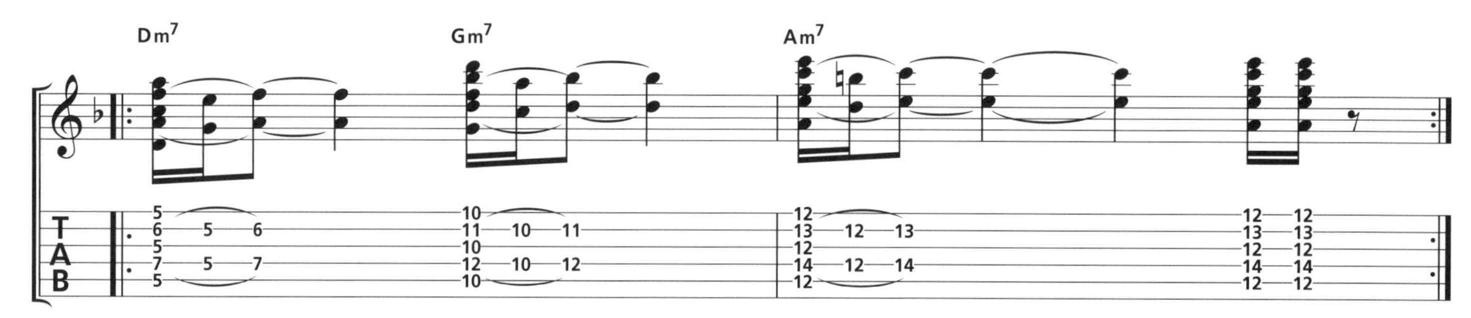

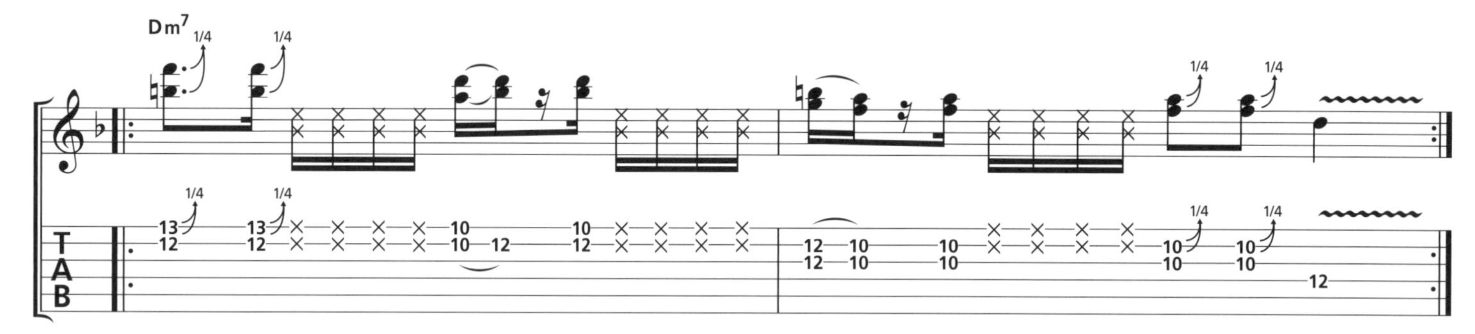

3. Jazz/Latin/Blues: crossing strings and octaves

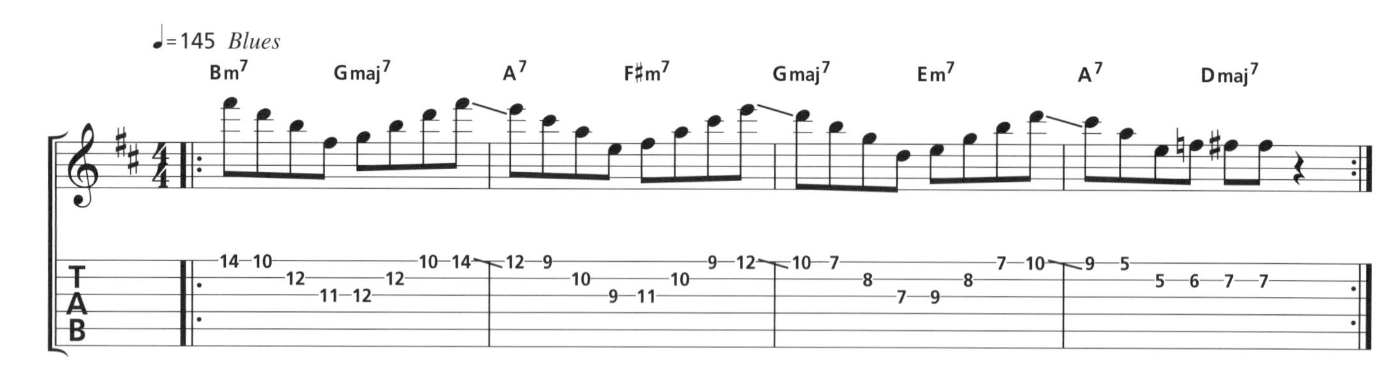

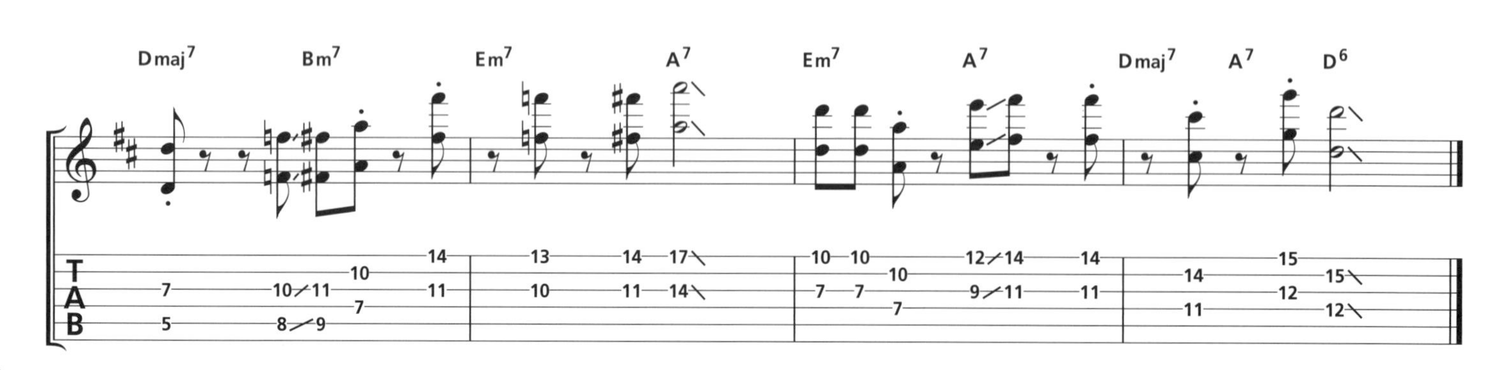

Quick Study Piece

Tracks 19 & 20

At this grade you will be asked to prepare and play a short Quick Study Piece (QSP). Printed below are three examples of the type of QSP you are likely to receive in the exam. You will be shown the test and played the track with the *notated parts played*. Any bars that require improvisation will not be demonstrated. You will then have three minutes to study the test. The backing track will be played twice more. You will be allowed to practise during the first playing of the backing track, with the notated parts now absent, before playing it to the examiner on the second playing of the backing track.

The style of your QSP is determined by the stylistic study you selected in the technical exercise section. The QSP is in the form of a lead sheet and it is up to you to create your own interpretation of the music in the parts marked for improvisation.

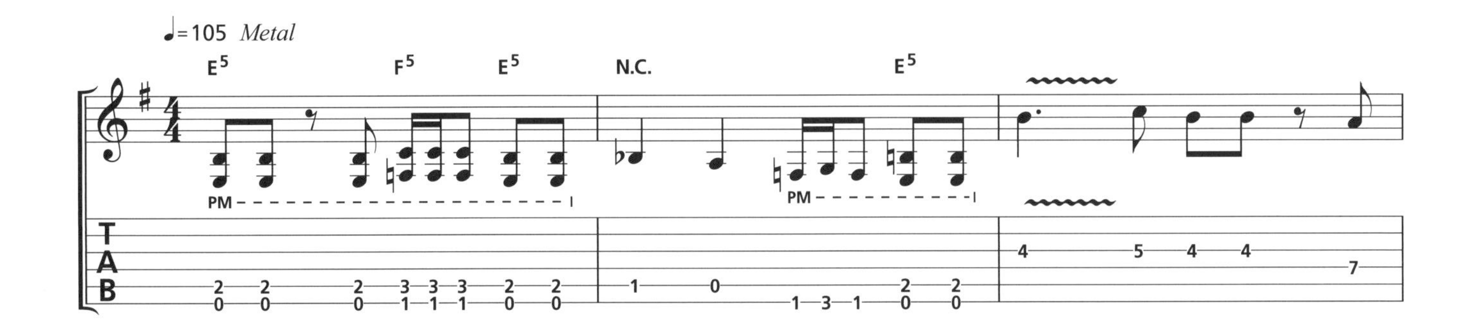

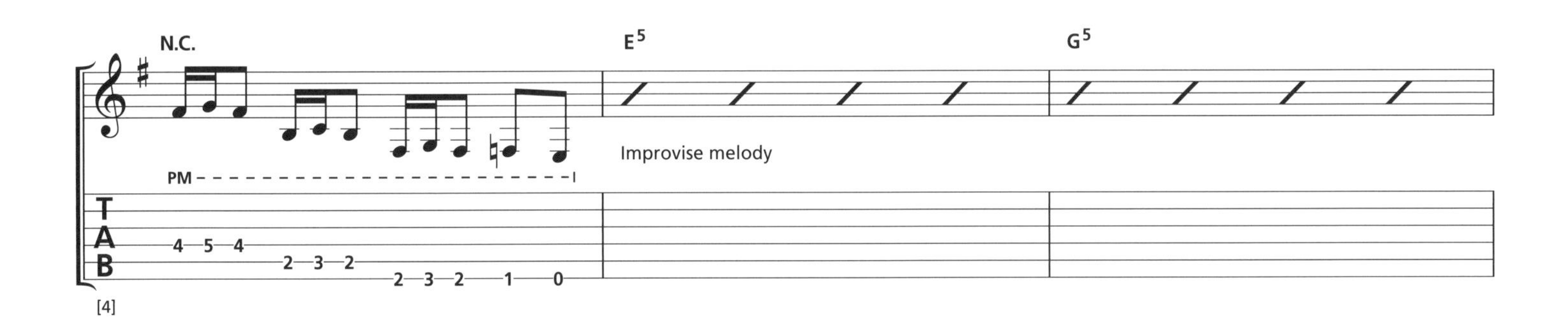

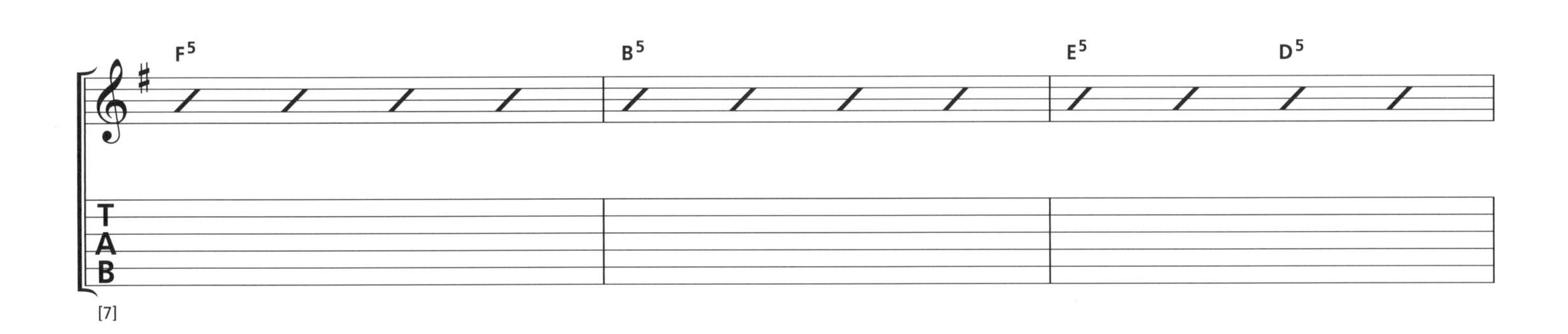

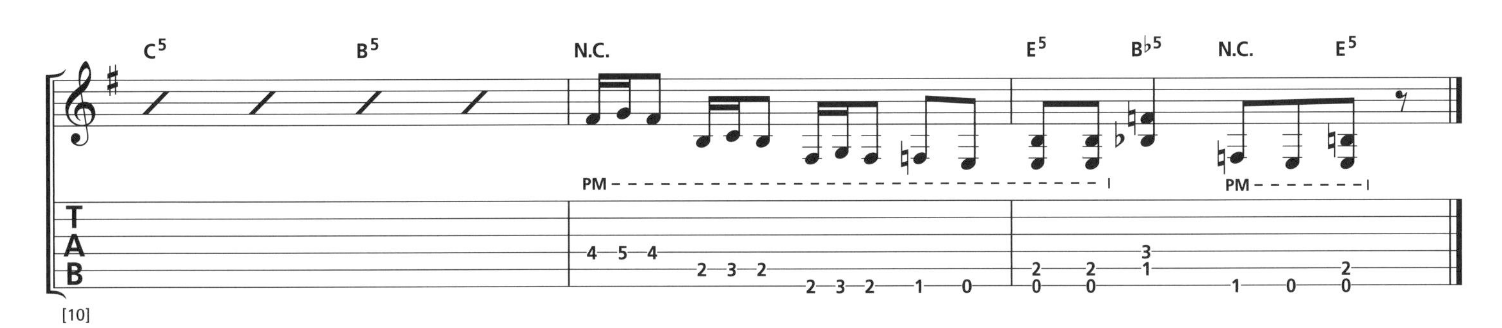

♩=90 Funk
N.C.
T
A
B
5 5 3 5
5 5 3 4 3
5 5 3 5

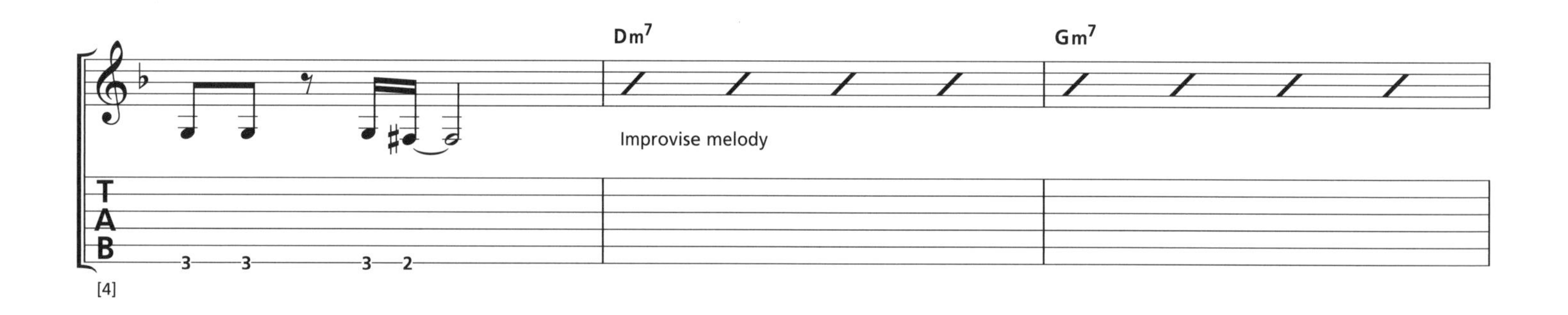
Dm7
Gm7
Improvise melody
T
A
B
3 3 3 2
[4]

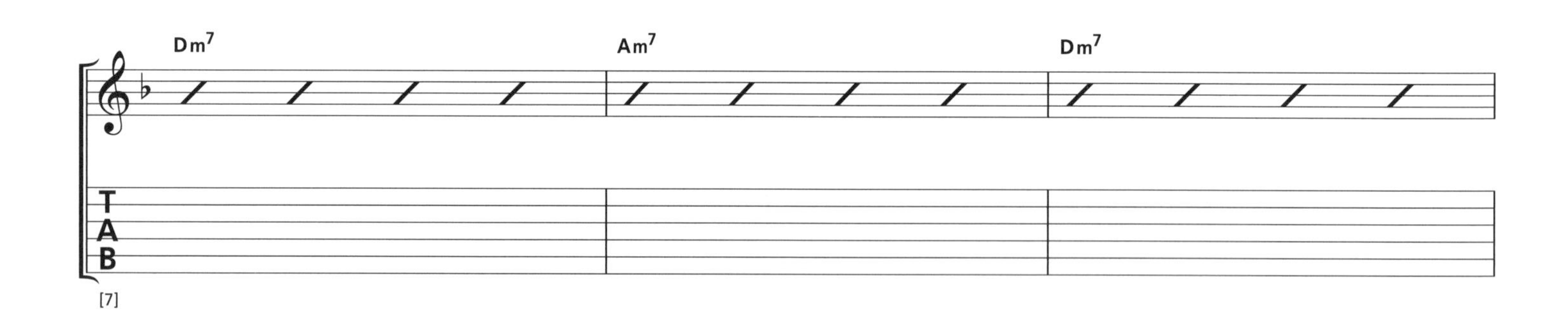
Dm7
Am7
Dm7
T
A
B
[7]

B♭
C
N.C.
T
A
B
5 5 3 5
5 5 3 4 5
[10]

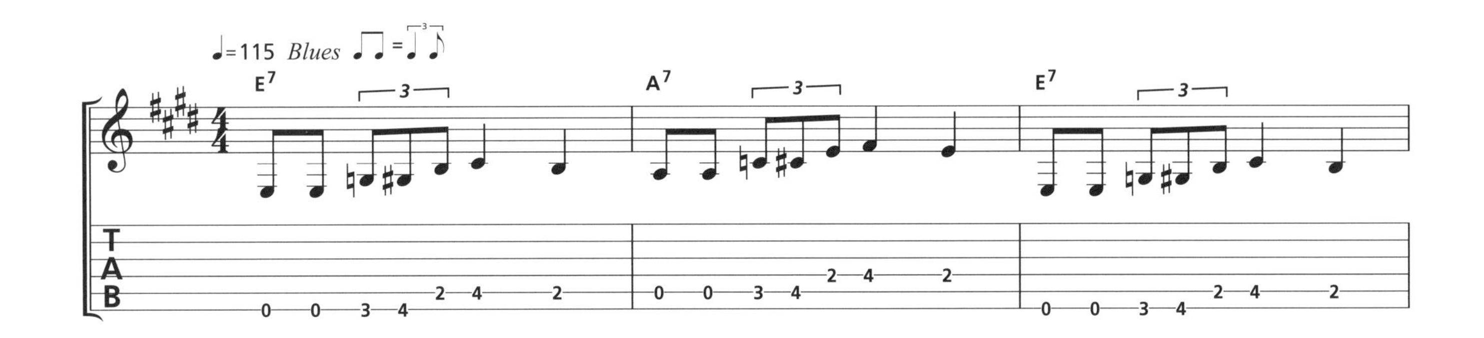
♩=115 Blues
E7
A7
E7
T
A
B

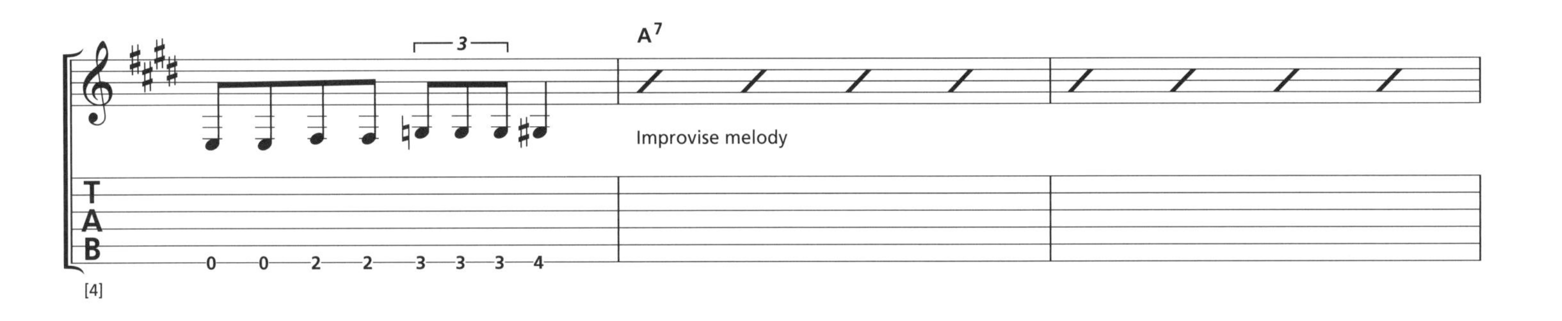
A7
Improvise melody
T
A
B
[4]

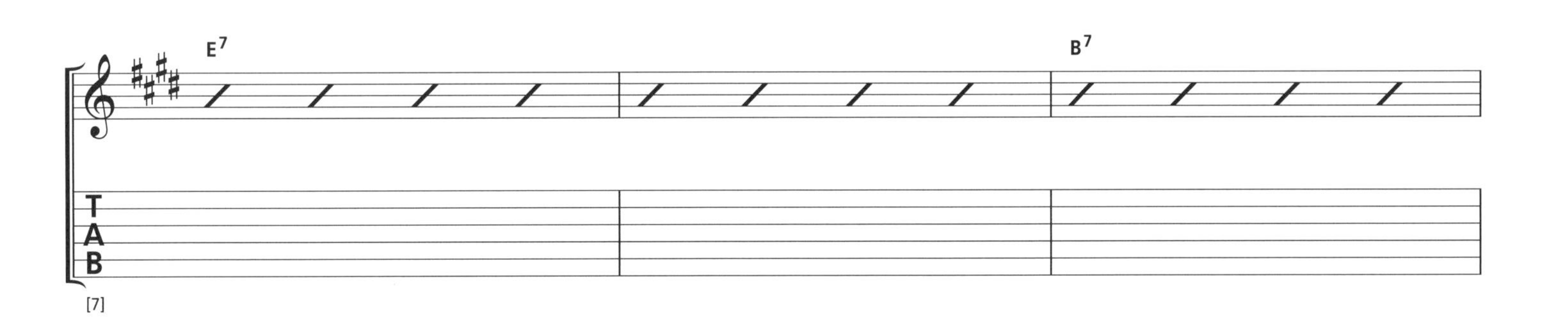
E7
B7
T
A
B
[7]

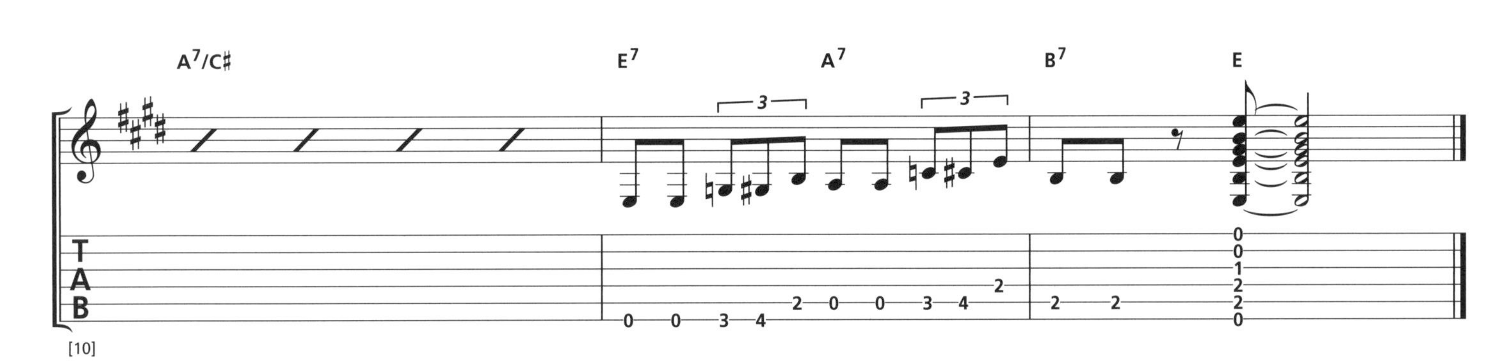
A7/C♯
E7
A7
B7
E
T
A
B
[10]

Ear Tests

There are two ear tests in this grade. The examiner will play each test to you twice. You will find one example of each type of test printed below.

Test 1: Melodic Recall

The examiner will play you a two bar melody with a bass and drum backing using either the A major pentatonic, C minor pentatonic or A natural minor scales. The first note of the melody will be *either* the root note *or* fifth and the first interval will be *either* ascending *or* descending. You will play the melody back on your instrument. You will hear the test twice.

Each time the test is played the sequence is: count-in, root note, count-in, melody. There will be a short gap for you to practise after you have heard the test for the second time. You will hear the count-in and root note for the third time followed by a *vocal* count-in and you will then play the melody to the bass and drum backing. The tempo is ♩=90.

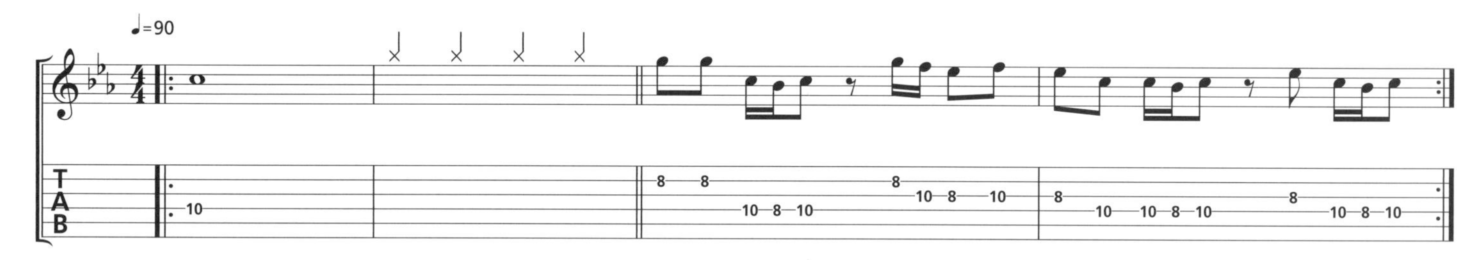

Test 2: Harmonic Recall

The examiner will play you a tonic chord followed by a four bar chord sequence in the key of A major played to a bass and drum backing. The sequence will use the I, ii, iii, IV, V and vi chords. The ii, iii and vi chords can be either minor or minor 7th chords. You will be asked to play the chord sequence to the bass and drum backing in the rhythm shown in the example below. This rhythm will be used in all examples of this test given in the exam. You will then be asked to identify the sequence you have played to the examiner, including any chord extensions. You will hear the test twice.

Each time the test is played the sequence is: count-in, tonic, count-in, chords. There will be a short gap for you to practise after you have heard the test for the second time. You will hear the count-in and tonic for the third time followed by a *vocal* count-in and you will then play the chords to the bass and drum backing. You should then name the chord sequence, including the chord type and any extensions. The tempo is ♩=90.

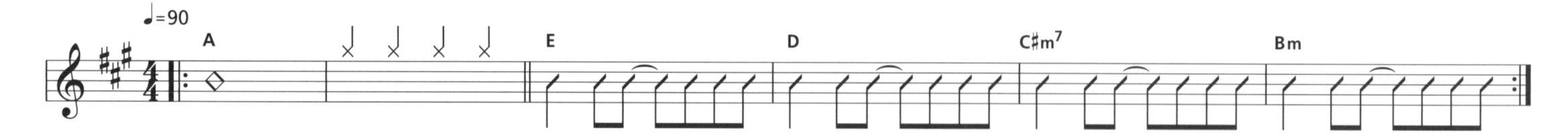

General Musicianship Questions

In this part of the exam you will be asked five questions. Four of these questions will be about general music knowledge and the fifth question will be asked about your instrument.

Music Knowledge

The examiner will ask you four music knowledge questions based on a piece of music that you have played in the exam. You will nominate the piece of music about which the questions will be asked. In this grade you will be asked to identify and demonstrate your answers on your instrument as directed by the examiner. The scale question at the end of the list of subjects is mandatory.

In Grade 7 you will be asked:

- The names of pitches
- Any expressive musical marking found in the piece such as palm muting, accents, staccato, legato, vibrato, natural and artificial harmonics
- Any dynamic marking found in the piece
- One type of scale that can be used appropriately in the solo section of the piece you have played and its relation to the underlying harmony of the piece

Instrument Knowledge

The examiner will also ask you one question regarding your instrument.

In Grade 7 you will be asked to explain and demonstrate:

- Where to find the same pitch on two different strings
- The function of the volume and tone controls on your guitar
- The set up for the tone required for the piece you have played on the amp
- How to create changes in tone in a song

Further Information

Tips on how to approach this part of this exam can be found in the *Syllabus Guide* for guitar, the Rockschool *Guitar Companion Guide* and on the Rockschool website: *www.rockschool.co.uk*. The Introduction to Tone, a comprehensive explanation of guitar tones, can be found at the back of each grade book and the tone guide to each piece is in the appropriate Walkthrough.

Entering Rockschool Exams

Entering a Rockschool exam is easy. You may enter either online at *www.rockschool.co.uk* or by downloading and filling in an exam entry form. Information on current exam fees can be obtained from Rockschool online or by calling +44 (0)845 460 4747.

- You should enter for your exam when you feel ready.
- You may enter for any one of the three examination periods shown below with their closing dates:

Examination periods

PERIOD	DURATION	CLOSING DATE
Period A	1st February to 31st March	1st December
Period B	1st May to 31st July	1st April
Period C	23rd October to 15th December	1st October

These dates apply from 1st September 2012 until further notice

- The full Rockschool examination terms and conditions can be downloaded from our website. The information shown below is a summary.
- Please complete your entry with the information required. Fill in the type and level of exam and instrument, along with the examination period and year. Paper entry forms should be sent with a cheque or postal order (payable to Rockschool Ltd) to the address shown on the entry form. Entry forms sent by post will be acknowledged either by letter or email, while all entries made online will automatically be acknowledged by email.
- Applications received after the expiry of the closing date, whether made by post or online, may be accepted subject to the payment of a late fee.
- Rockschool will allocate your exam to a specific centre and you will receive notification of the exam showing a date, location and time, as well as advice on what to bring to the centre. We endeavour to give you four weeks notice ahead of your exam date.
- You should inform Rockschool of any cancellations or alterations to the schedule as soon as you can because it may not be possible to transfer entries from one centre, or one period, to another without the payment of an additional fee.
- Please bring your music book and CD to the exam. You may use photocopied music if this helps you avoid awkward page turns. The examiner will sign each book during each examination. Please note, you may be barred from taking an exam if you use someone else's music.
- You should aim to arrive for your exam 15 minutes before the time stated on the schedule. Guitarists and bass players should get ready to enter the exam room by taking their instrument from its case and tuning up. This will help with the smooth running of each exam day.
- Each Grade 7 exam is scheduled to last 30 minutes. You can use a small proportion of this time to set up and check the sound levels.
- You will receive a copy of the examiner's marksheet two to three weeks after the exam. If you have passed you will also receive a Rockschool certificate of achievement.

Guitar Grade 7 Marking Schemes

Grade Exams | Grades 6–8

ELEMENT	PASS	MERIT	DISTINCTION
Performance Piece 1	12–14 out of 20	15–17 out of 20	18+ out of 20
Performance Piece 2	12–14 out of 20	15–17 out of 20	18+ out of 20
Performance Piece 3	12–14 out of 20	15–17 out of 20	18+ out of 20
Technical Exercises	9–10 out of 15	11–12 out of 15	13+ out of 15
Quick Study Piece	6 out of 10	7–8 out of 10	9+ out of 10
Ear Tests	6 out of 10	7–8 out of 10	9+ out of 10
General Musicianship Questions	3 out of 5	4 out of 5	5 out of 5
TOTAL MARKS	60%+	74%+	90%+

Performance Certificates | Grades 1–8

ELEMENT	PASS	MERIT	DISTINCTION
Performance Piece 1	12–14 out of 20	15–17 out of 20	18+ out of 20
Performance Piece 2	12–14 out of 20	15–17 out of 20	18+ out of 20
Performance Piece 3	12–14 out of 20	15–17 out of 20	18+ out of 20
Performance Piece 4	12–14 out of 20	15–17 out of 20	18+ out of 20
Performance Piece 5	12–14 out of 20	15–17 out of 20	18+ out of 20
TOTAL MARKS	60%+	75%+	90%+

Introduction to Tone

A large part of an effective guitar performance is selecting the right tone. The electric guitar's sound is subject to a wide range of variables, and this guide outlines the basic controls present on most amplifiers as well as the common variations between models. There is also a basic overview of pickups and the effect their location on the guitar has on tone. Finally, it covers the differences between the types of distortion, which is crucial to getting your basic sound right.

At Grade 7 the tone may change within the course of a piece. You should aim to use a tone that is stylistically appropriate and you may bring your own equipment to the exam room for this purpose. There is a tone guide at the start of each walkthrough to help you.

Basic amplifier controls

Most amplifiers come with a standard set of controls that are the same as, or very similar to, the diagram below. It's important to understand what each control is and the effect that it has on your guitar's tone.

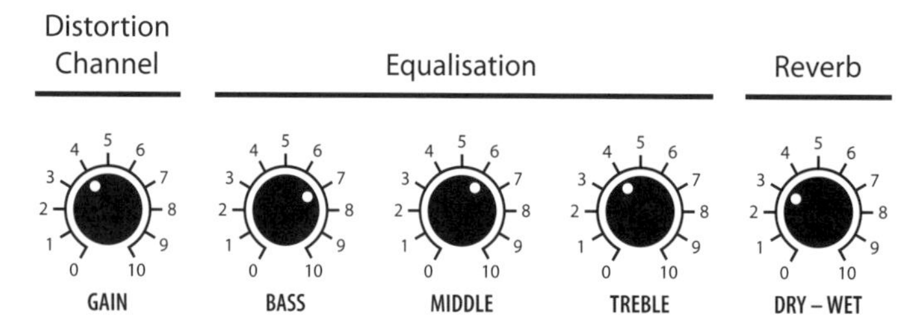

- **Channel (Clean/Distortion)**
  Most amplifiers have two channels that can be selected either by a switch on the amp or a footswitch. One channel is usually 'clean' while the other can be driven harder to create a distorted (or 'dirty') tone. If your amp doesn't have two channels, look at the 'variation of basic controls' below to see how to get clean and dirty tones from a one channel amp.

- **Gain**
  In simple terms, the gain determines how hard you drive the amp. This governs how distorted the dirty (also called 'drive', 'overdrive', or 'distortion') channel is and acts as a second volume control on the clean channel (though a high gain setting will distort even the clean channel).

- **Bass**
  This adjusts the lowest frequencies. Boost it to add warmth and reduce or 'cut' it if your sound is muddy or woolly.

- **Middle**
  This is the most important equalisation (often shortened to just 'EQ') control. Most of the guitar's tonal character is found in the mid-range so adjusting this control has a lot of impact upon your tone. Boosting it with a dirty sound will create a more classic rock tone while cutting it will produce a more metal one.

- **Treble**
  This adjusts the high frequencies. Boost it to add brightness and cut it if the sound is too harsh or brittle.

- **Reverb**
  Short for 'reverberation'. This artificially recreates the ambience of your guitar in a large room, usually a hall. This dial controls the balance between the 'dry' (the sound without the reverb) and 'wet' (the sound with the reverb) sounds.

Variations of basic controls

The diagram above shows the most common amp controls. There are many variations to this basic setup, which can often be confusing. The following section is a breakdown of some of the other amp controls you may encounter:

- **Presence control**
  Sometimes this dial replaces the 'middle' control and other times it appears in addition to it. It adjusts the higher mid-range frequencies (those found between the 'middle' and 'treble' dials).

- **No reverb control**
  Reverb can be a nice addition to your guitar tone but it's not essential. Don't be concerned if your amp doesn't have a reverb control.

- **Volume, gain, master setup**
  Single channel amplifiers often have an extra volume control (in addition to the master volume) located next to the gain control. For clean sounds, keep the gain set low and the volume similarly low and use the master control for overall volume. If the master control is on 10 and you require more level, turn the volume control up. However, you may find that this starts to distort as you reach the higher numbers.

  To get a distorted tone, turn the volume down low and the gain up until you get the amount of distortion you require. Regulate the overall level with master volume. If the master control is on 10 and you require more level simply turn the volume up. In this case, however, you may find you lose clarity before you reach maximum.

Pickups

Entire books have been devoted to the intricacies of pickups. However, three basic pieces of information will help you understand a lot about your guitar tone:

- **Singlecoils**
  These narrow pickups are fitted to many guitars. The Fender Stratocaster is the most famous guitar fitted with singlecoils. They produce a bright, cutting sound that can sound a little thin in some situations, especially heavier styles of rock music.

- **Humbuckers**
  This type of pickup was originally designed to remove or 'buck' the hum produced by singlecoil pickups, hence the name. They produce a warm, mellow sound compared to singlecoil pickups but have a tendency to sound a little muddy in some situations. They are usually identifiable because they are twice the width of a singlecoil pickup. The Gibson Les Paul is a well-known guitar fitted with humbucking pickups.

- **Pickup location**
  Basically, pickups located near the guitar's neck will have the warmest sound and those located near the bridge will have the brightest sound.

Different types of 'dirty' tones

There are lots of different words to describe the 'dirty' guitar sounds. In fact, all the sounds are 'distortions' of the clean tone, which can be confusing when you consider there's a 'type' of distortion called 'distortion'. Below is a simplified breakdown of the three main types of dirty sounds, plus some listening material to help you through this tonal minefield:

- **Overdrive**
  This is the 'mildest' form of distortion. It can be quite subtle and only evident when the guitar is played strongly. It can be also be full-on and aggressive.
  Hear it on: Cream – 'Sunshine Of Your Love', AC/DC – 'Back In Black', Oasis – 'Cigarettes and Alcohol'.

- **Distortion**
  This is usually associated with heavier styles of music. It's dense and the most extreme of the dirty tones and is usually associated with heavy styles of music.
  Hear it on: Metallica – 'Enter Sandman', Avenged Sevenfold – 'Bat Country', Bon Jovi – 'You Give Love A Bad Name'.

- **Fuzz**
  As the name implies, fuzz is a broken, 'fuzzy' sound. It was popular in the 1960s but, while still evident in certain genres, it's less common now.
  Hear it on: Jimi Hendrix Experience – 'Purple Haze', The Kinks – 'You Really Got Me'.

Guitar Notation Explained

THE MUSICAL STAVE shows pitches and rhythms and is divided by lines into bars. Pitches are named after the first seven letters of the alphabet.

TABLATURE graphically represents the guitar fingerboard. Each horizontal line represents a string, and each number represents a fret.

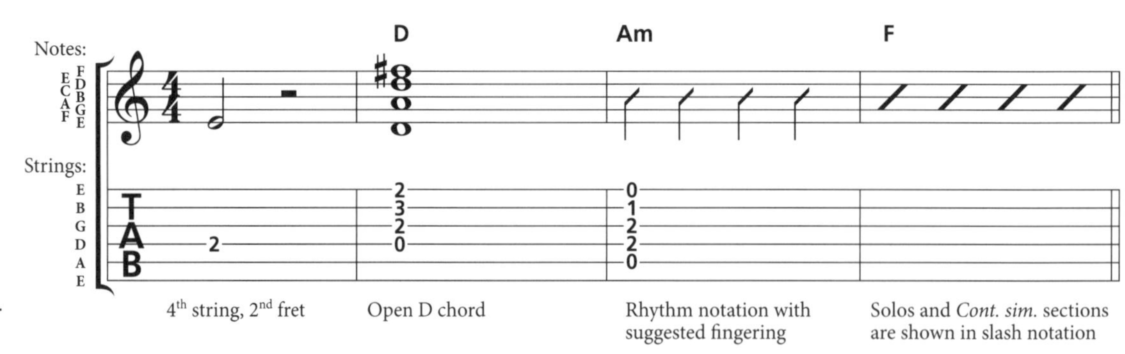

4th string, 2nd fret
Open D chord
Rhythm notation with suggested fingering
Solos and *Cont. sim.* sections are shown in slash notation

Definitions For Special Guitar Notation

HAMMER ON: Pick the lower note, then sound the higher note by fretting it without picking.

PULL OFF: Pick the higher note then sound the lower note by lifting the finger without picking.

SLIDE: Pick the first note and slide to the next. If the line connects (as below) the second note ***is not*** repicked.

GLISSANDO: Slide off of a note at the end of its rhythmic value. The note that follows ***is*** repicked.

STRING BENDS: Pick the first note then bend (or release the bend) to the pitch indicated in brackets.

VIBRATO: Vibrate the note by bending and releasing the string smoothly and continuously.

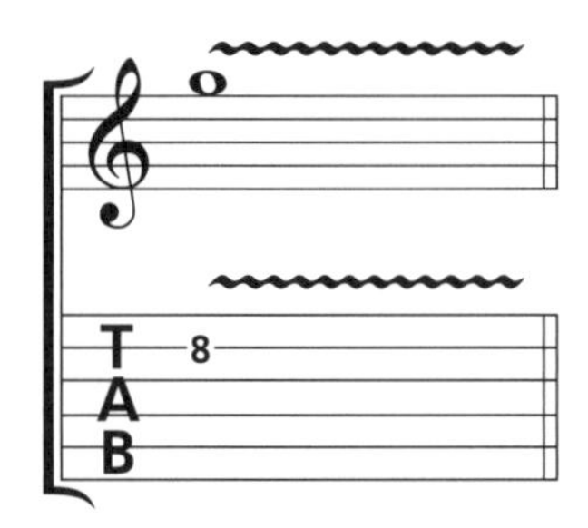

TRILL: Rapidly alternate between the two bracketed notes by hammering on and pulling off.

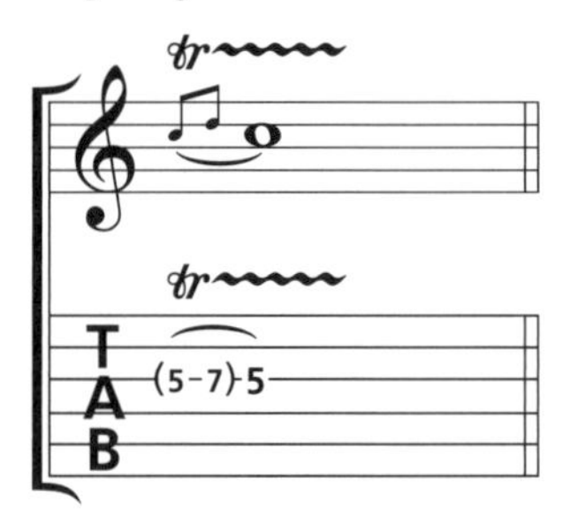

NATURAL HARMONICS: Lightly touch the string above the indicated fret then pick to sound a harmonic.

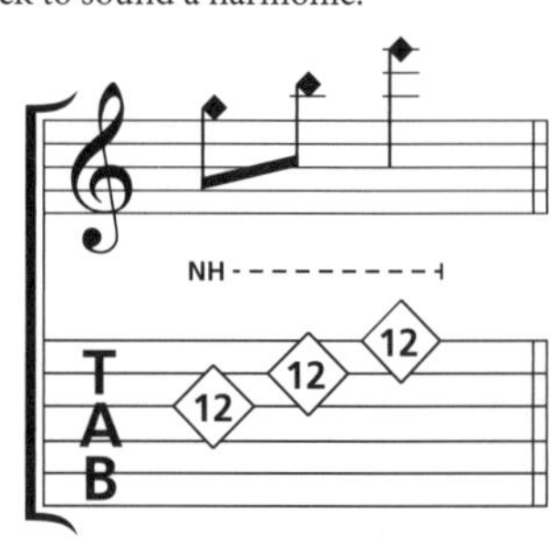

PINCHED HARMONICS: Bring the thumb of the picking hand into contact with the string immediately after the pick.

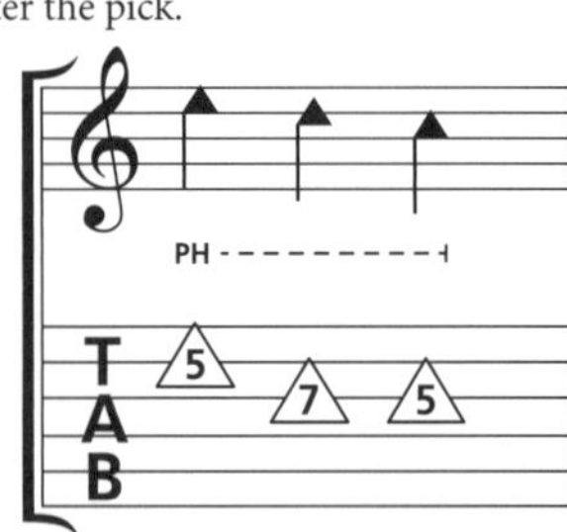

PICK HAND TAP: Strike the indicated note with a finger from the picking hand. Usually followed by a pull off.

FRET HAND TAP: As pick hand tap, but use fretting hand. Usually followed by a pull off or hammer on.

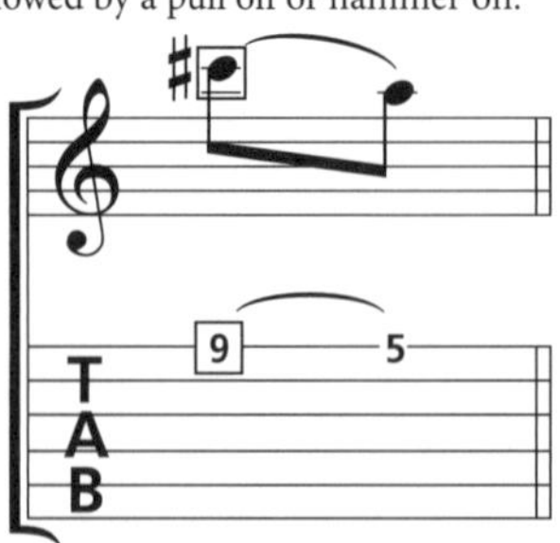

QUARTER TONE BEND: Pick the note indicated and bend the string up by a quarter tone.

PRE-BENDS: Before picking the note, bend the string from the fret indicated between the staves, to the equivalent pitch indicated in brackets in the TAB

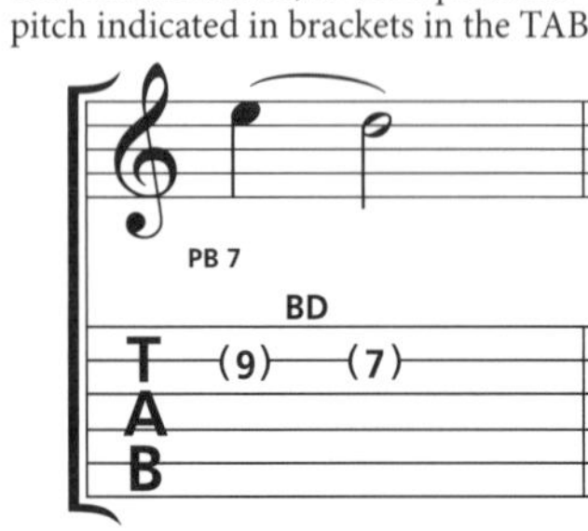

WHAMMY BAR BEND: Use the whammy bar to bend notes to the pitches indicated in brackets in the TAB

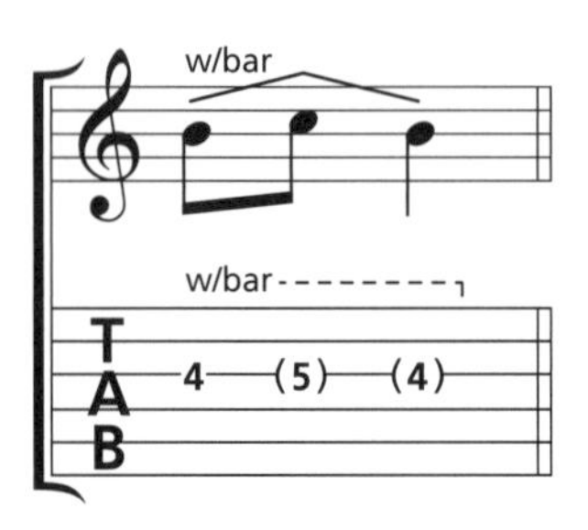

D.𝄋. al Coda

- Go back to the sign (𝄋), then play until the bar marked **To Coda 𝄌** then skip to the section marked **𝄌 Coda**.

D.C. al Fine

- Go back to the beginning of the song and play until the bar marked **Fine** (end).

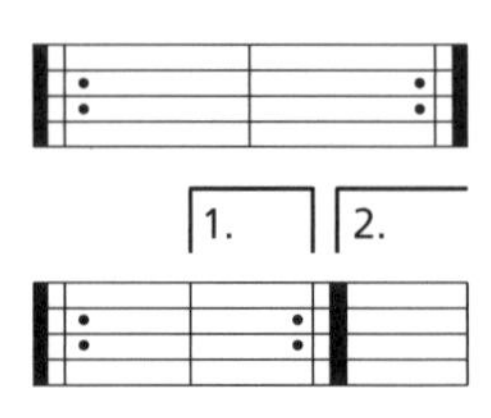

- Repeat bars between signs.
- When a repeated section has different endings, play the first ending only the first time and the second ending only the second time.

GRADE 8 PREVIEW

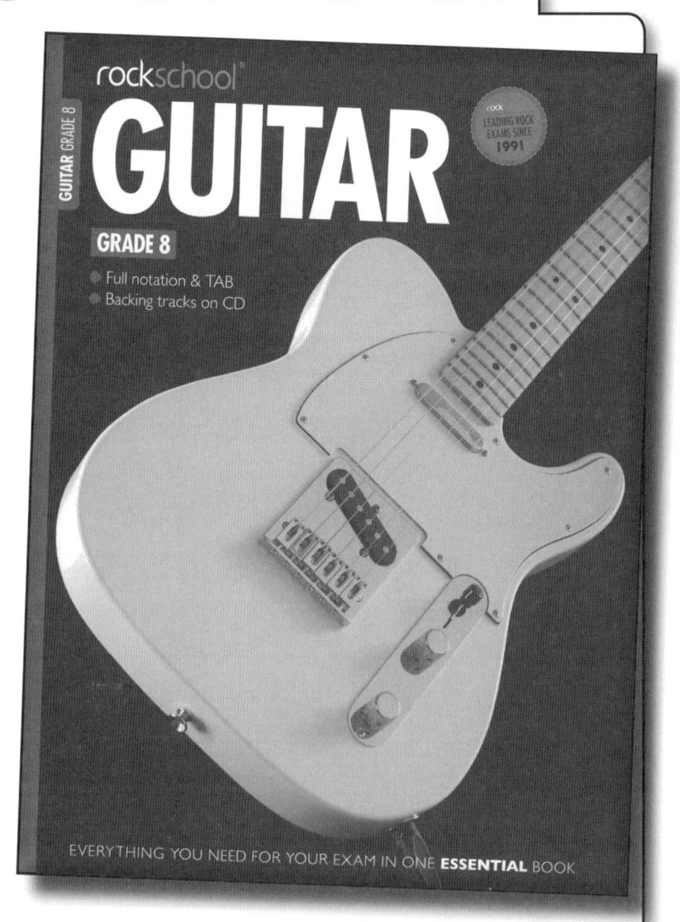

SONG TITLE:	NOSSO SAMBA
GENRE:	SAMBA
TEMPO:	110 BPM
KEY:	G MAJOR
TECH FEATURES:	OCTAVE MELODIES FINGERPICKED CHORDS 16TH NOTE STRUMMING
COMPOSER:	NOAM LEDERMAN
PERSONNEL:	NOAM LEDERMAN (DRUMS) HENRY THOMAS (BASS) STUART RYAN (GTR) KISHON KHAN (KEYS) FERGUS GERRAND (PERC) CHRIS WEBSTER (TROMBONE)

OVERVIEW

'Nosso Samba' is written in the style of classic Brazilian artists such as the revered Antonio Carlos Jobim and Gilberto Gil, and the modern day samba group Nosso Trio. It features octave melodies, fingerpicked chords and 16th note strumming patterns among its techniques.

STYLE FOCUS

Since the bossa nova era of the 1950s, samba has had much in common with jazz. A lot of the music is improvised so a familiarity with playing over standards and changes will be of benefit to a student of the Brazilian music 'Nosso Samba' is based on. The bossa nova rhythm style is usually played with thumb and fingers, although you could achieve the same effect using a combination of pick and fingers.

THE BIGGER PICTURE

Samba is the rhythmic, syncopated music of Brazil with its roots in the African culture of the country's black population. The first samba record is believed to be a song called 'Pelo Telefono' that was released in 1917, and gave the style its first significant exposure outside of the favelas (slums). Early samba relied on the power of drums and percussion, and was revered for its raw energy rather than musical sophistication.

However, this changed in the 1950s when young middle class suburbanites like João Gilberto and Jobim brought in supple melodies and jazz influenced harmonies. This new style, or 'bossa nova', exposed Brazilian music to the world; its best known song is 'The Girl From Ipanema', which was translated into English and performed by Frank Sinatra.

More recently, Nosso Trio have developed modern samba and inspired instrumentalists from every corner of the planet to explore Brazilian music. The trio's guitarist, Nelson Faria, attended Los Angeles' Guitar Institute Of Technology where he studied under fusion guitarists Scott Henderson and Frank Gambale. He has since written books and produced videos about Brazilian guitar playing.

RECOMMENDED LISTENING

Gilberto's *Chega De Saudade* (1959) is a bossa nova classic. To hear how Brazilian music changed in the 1960s, listen to *Caetano Veloso* (1968) by Caetano Veloso. Finally, Nosso Trio's modern take on samba can be heard on their 2006 debut *Vento Bravo*.

Nosso Samba (Grade 8 Preview)

Noam Lederman

G6
Gmaj9
G6
Gmaj9
[25]
C
G6
Gmaj9
G6
Gmaj9
[29]
G6
Gmaj9
G6
Gmaj9
[33]
Cadd9
C
Cmaj7
C
[37]
Am7
Cm7
F9
[41]
G6
Gmaj9
G6
Gmaj9
Bm7♭5
[45]

Guitar Grade 7

D
E7♭9
Am7
D7♭9
Fmaj9
Gm7
C7♭9
Fmaj7
Am7
Dm9
Dm7
A♭
B♭7
Gm
A♭maj7
Am7♭5
[49]
[53]
[57]
[61]
[65]
[69]

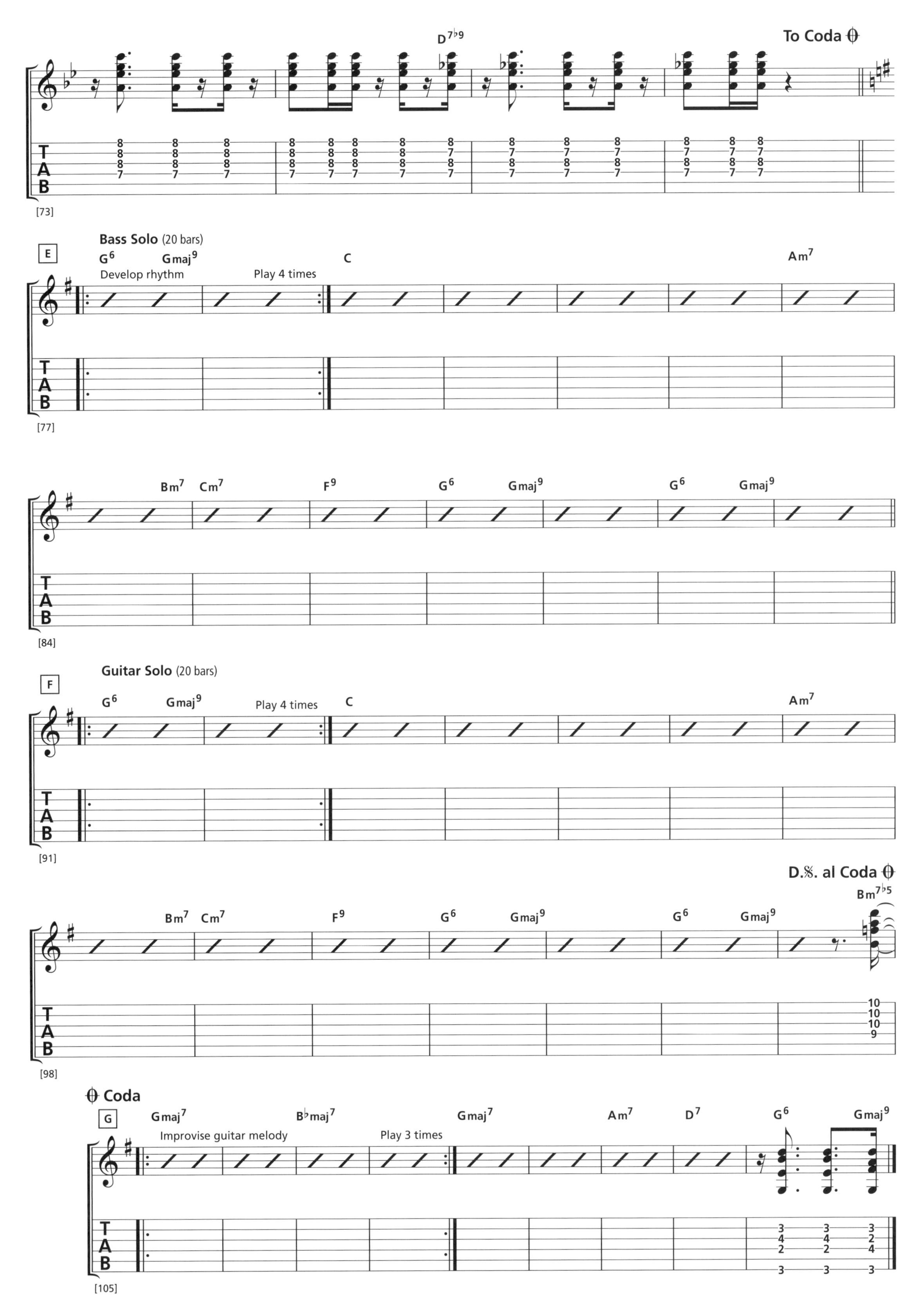
D7♭9
To Coda
[73]
Bass Solo (20 bars)
E
G6
Gmaj9
Develop rhythm
Play 4 times
C
Am7
[77]
Bm7
Cm7
F9
G6
Gmaj9
G6
Gmaj9
[84]
Guitar Solo (20 bars)
F
G6
Gmaj9
Play 4 times
C
Am7
[91]
D.%. al Coda
Bm7♭5
Bm7
Cm7
F9
G6
Gmaj9
G6
Gmaj9
[98]
Coda
G
Gmaj7
Improvise guitar melody
B♭maj7
Play 3 times
Gmaj7
Am7
D7
G6
Gmaj9
[105]

Guitar Grade 7

Walkthrough (Grade 8 Preview)

Amp Settings

Aim for a clean tone that's full and warm. Using your guitar's neck pickup will help with this. Boost the bass but don't let the sound become too muddy. Roll off the middle and treble if you feel the sound is too harsh. Reverb, if available, will greatly enhance the mood of this piece.

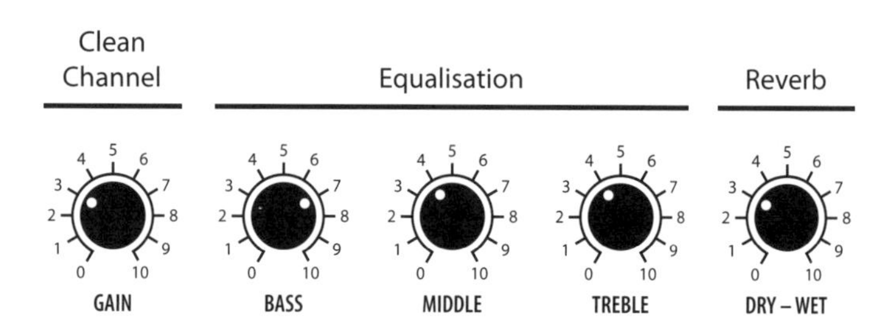

A & B sections (Bars 1–28)

The A and B sections are based on a fingerpicked chordal groove. The A section is a drum solo while the B section involves the bass playing the melody.

Bars 10–11 | *Cuíca*

The A section ends with an imitation of a cuíca, which is a high pitched sounding Brazilian drum. This unique sound is achieved by quickly sliding up from several frets below each note. This quick movement is challenging and you should ensure that the destination notes are played in time.

C Section (Bars 29–48)

The C section consists of an octave melody. Syncopated rhythms and fast position shifts make this a tricky section.

Bars 29–47 | *Sliding octaves*

Approach sliding octaves in the same way as playing powerchords and barre chords: lock your fingers in position and move the fretting hand as a unit rather than dealing with individual finger placement.

D Section (Bars 49–76)

This intense rhythmic part uses several altered chords played on the first four strings of the guitar.

Bars 49–76 | *Complex rhythms*

This rhythm will take some preparation to master. Work slowly while counting 16th notes as shown in Fig. 1. Aim to feel the rhythm rather than counting it to help your performance sound more convincing. A 16th note strumming pattern will help you keep the pulse throughout the numerous syncopated rhythms.

E & F Sections (Bars 77–104)

The E section is the bass solo. The F section is a guitar solo.

Bars 77–90 | *Accompanying a solo*

While you must create an interesting part to accompany the bass solo, your primary goal is to support the soloist.

Bars 91–104 | *Guitar solo*

The G major scale will work throughout bars 77–84 and the C dorian mode for bars 85–86. Many jazz players opt for the lydian mode over the major scale because its ♯4 interval introduces tension that the major scale does not provide. If you wish to try this approach use G lydian in bars 77–78 and C lydian in bars 79–84.

G Section (Bars 105–113)

The G section is another opportunity for you to create your own part. This time, improvise a melody that complements the two-hand tapped part the bassist is playing.

Bars 105–113 | *Gmaj⁷–B♭maj⁷ chord change*

Rather than changing scale position every time the chord changes (which may sound disjointed), stay in the same position and adjust the relevant notes every two bars. Start in G major then adjust the F♯, B and E to F♮, B♭ and E♭ respectively (Fig. 2).

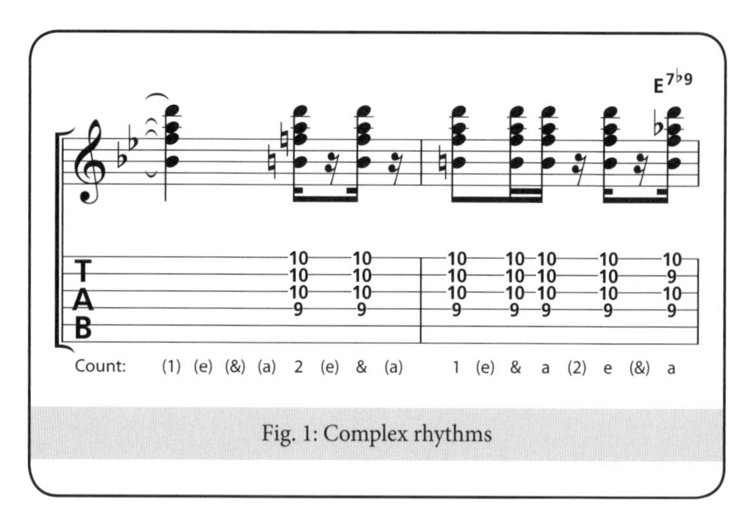

Fig. 1: Complex rhythms

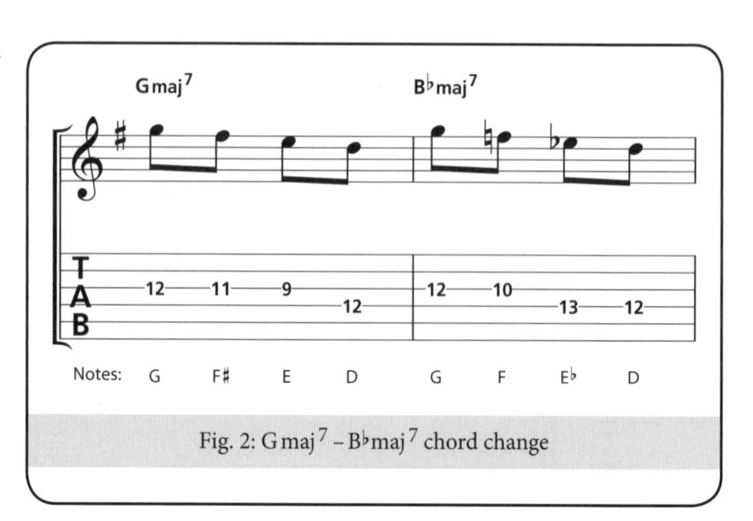

Fig. 2: Gmaj⁷ – B♭maj⁷ chord change